FOREWORD

Welcome to numismatics! Few leisure interests have so much to offer. A world of past and present can be at your fingertips through a few dollars invested in well-chosen coins. Thrilling chapters of Canada's past live again in her early tokens, and her fine decimal strikings reflect ten decades of accelerated growth. If the twentieth century be Canada's, then its seventh decade is numismatics', for never before has the hobby witnessed such an upsurge of popular interest, and Canadian numismatic traditions date back many years.

Numismatics is a broad area, for it has come to include the study and collecting of such monetary forms as coins, tokens, and paper money, and of medals. By far the greatest collecting interest in this country is in the silver, nickel and bronze coinage best known to all of us, and thousands of new coin enthusiasts are specializing in the dates and varieties of the familiar series with which we make change.

All Canada would seem to have become "coin conscious," and virtually overnight, Coin Clubs have sprung up in over one hundred communities. A young, vigorous national organization — the Canadian Numismatic Association — has enrolled over 6,500 in little more than ten years. Coins enjoy a brisk market, journals and societies flourish, and enthusiasm is at an all-time high. Canada's diverse numismatic series, intelligently collected, can provide more than enough for all. This is a good time to be a coin collector, and the newcomer is assured a warm welcome as he enters Canada's growing numismatic ranks.

Coin collecting is a very old hobby, but only in the increased leisure of the past decade has it found truly widespread appeal. The accessibility of clubs, periodicals, catalogues, albums and coin folders has made coin study easy, pleasant and personally rewarding. Educators and youth leaders have encouraged collecting as a discipline in orderliness and perseverance, and coin enthusiasts of all ages have come to value the hobby for its dividends in pleasure and relaxation, and for the fraternal good fellowship which permeates its ranks.

Age—Rarity—Value

Coins are fascinating—but like other things which require specialized knowledge for full appreciation, coins are grossly misunderstood. "It is old: therefore, it must be valuable"— this you hear so often, and the reasoning is wholly wrong. Roman coppers, older than the Christian calendar, are being sold for fifty cents, while thousands of dollars may be paid for a coin issued in the last forty years! Value, economics teaches us, depends upon supply and demand. Very old coinage you might expect to have all but vanished, but a coin proves all but indestructible; unless melted down it will persist over the centuries. No one ever throws away money, so practically every home has a few odds and ends of old coins. Age need not imply rarity, so there are old coins which are common and recent strikings which prove remarkably scarce. A coin is rare when relatively few specimens are in existence, so rarity relates to the supply side of supply and demand.

[3]

Strangely, a scarce piece may not command a high price. "Key" coins needed to complete popular series are assured of a ready market while other items may wait for years on a dealer's shelf. Mintage of a few thousands or tens of thousands in issues such as the silver dollar results in high valuations, while a similar release of commemorative medals might glut the market. To some extent, different series may go "out of fashion," and demand slacken. Happily the current trend in numismatic interest has extended to most series, but especially to familiar "decimal coinage," where thousands of Canadians are searching their pocket change for scarce varieties, responding to the high prices being paid for the more elusive types.

Rarities make the headlines and get the attention at coin shows, but are only one part of the story. Collections which are interesting and instructive can be built without expensive rarities — which is the reason so many new collectors of modest income can find fascination in numismatics today. Coins from circulation, or inexpensive tokens may be the start of a first-rate collection. Appreciation of Canada's great numismatic heritage convinces us that the worth of a coin cannot be gauged merely in dollars and cents.

Monetary Traditions

Money is a medium of exchange, a measure and repository of wealth. As such, money is as old as civilization, for the awkwardness of barter soon gives rise to some common denominator of trade. Wealth can be reckoned in terms of property, or cattle (whence the word *pecuniary*), or wives — but of the grain and shells and stones and beads that added to the great diversity of exchange media, none was to prove as effective as two precious metals of universal acceptance, silver and gold. Coins began as uniform samples of these precious metals, stamped by authority to attest to fineness and weight. In Biblical references we encounter a shift to monetary reckoning: the *thirty pieces of silver: the widow's mite*. Indeed, much of the glory of Greece and Rome is recorded on early coinage, and the pageant of the centuries is well documented in the numismatic cabinets of today.

The great names of history are preserved on a world's coinage, kings and queens, emperors, and heroes of peace and of war. Great kingdoms and tiny states immortalize important events on their medals and commemorative coins. Money itself makes history: the mighty Milled Dollar of Spain — the "piece of eight" of pirate lore — is woven into the story of many nations, for its circulation was universal, from the great Spanish mints of the Americas to the shops of Philadelphia and Melbourne, Halifax and Montreal. From the prestige of this international unit we derive the dollars of Canada and the United States, for when both nations decided to seek a national currency, it was found that citizens knew the Spanish dollar well.

But Canada's numismatic history is far older than the nation, and the colorful tokens which predate official coinage tell a fascinating story in themselves.

Colonial Coins and Tokens

Many collectors of Canadian coins commence their study at the point where most folders and albums begin, the year 1858. This is the date when a "decimal" coinage, based upon a dollar of 100 cents became the lawful exchange medium in the Province of Canada, replacing British sterling and a hodge-podge of foreign and private issues. It is the year when sizeable shipments of big bronze cents, and silver 5-cent, 10-cent and 20-cent pieces arrived from London's Tower Mint to set the style for what was to be Dominion of Canada coinage. These large shipments of 1858 coinage, supplemented by nine million additional cents dated 1859, proved sufficient to meet the needs of the Colony until after Confederation (1867), and the first coins of the federal union, the 1870 strikings, retained the characteristics of the 1858 provincial issue. The silver "fifth" (20 cents) was dropped, and replaced by the 25 cents, and the big 50-cent piece was inaugurated. The fine portraiture and attractive lines of the series which ensue quite naturally commend them to the new collector, and his familiarity with the denominations and main varieties makes him feel "at home" in his collecting. Earlier Canadian "money" consisted largely of private copper Tokens and British and foreign silver and gold, supplemented at times by private scrip and by the paper money of no less than 98 note-issuing banks. The tokens prove particularly interesting to the student and collector, and the fact that such a diversity of them remains accessible and in-expensive leaves no reason why the historic series should be ignored.

A coin is backed by government authority. A token, on the other hand, may be the issue of a bank, firm, or individual, and exists only because it fills a somewhat local monetary need. It circulates; doing so, it becomes money in the full economic sense. Canada has, through necessity, had great need of such tokens, for under the French regime and the English, little money cir-culated or stayed in the New World. The early *Habitant* was largely self-sufficient, and barter could serve most of his needs. But such growing urban centers as Halifax, St. John, Quebec, Montreal and Toronto required money, and gold and silver tended to flow out of the Colonies faster than it could be brought in. A cosmopolitan diversity of gold, silver and copper pieces passed through the tills of the seaports, but the total in the Colonies at any given time was quite small. Prince Edward Island's "holey dollar," the Milled Dol-lar of Spain with its centre punched out would not be accepted for inter-national trade. A similar situation existed with the "playing card money" of the French regime. In short, tokens had the advantage of staying where they were issued, and to that extent were a complete success. The advertising and political slogans of these series are fascinating — "Encourage Country Im-porters," "Fishery Rights for Newfoundland," "Pure Copper Preferable to Paper," "No Labour — No Bread," "Speed the Plough." Glance through the illustrations, the political tokens, the interesting "bouquet sous," and the price listings, and you will see a series from which a remarkable and inexpen-sive selection can be made. Add to these the unbelievable mixture of world coinage once found in Canadian circulation, and still unearthed from time to time in Canada's more historic regions, and you have the picture of the nation's money prior to introduction of decimal coinage in 1858. A far cry from today! Yet it is not too long ago to remember when British half-penny pieces cir-culated as cents, which they resembled, and the occasional shilling which passed at 25 cents, though it rated only 24, this as recently as World War II.

Tokens are still being issued, for bus fares, purchases, bridge tolls and for like specialized functions, and these modern issues need not be ignored; but gone forever is the day when the retail merchant could produce a wide variety of his community's change.

[5]

Decimal Coinages

"Try to find, in your change, a cent of every date since 1920...." This challenge has been the start of many a Canadian collection, and it reflects a trend. While it is traditional, in most parts of the world, for the numismatist to be concerned with principal coinage types, not series of dates, the popular practice in Canada and the United States has been definitely to seek and complete such series. There is widespread interest in studying the dates and varieties of familiar coin series, observing their relative availability, and searching for the best condition obtainable. Thousands do. A glance through mint statistics will explain the scarcity of such popular coins as the 1948 silver dollar, the 1890 and 1894 50 cents, and the 1946 Newfoundland five cents. Mint statistics do not always tell the whole story. Reported quantities struck sometimes are misleading. For example such rarities as the 1921 five and 50 cents became scarce when large surpluses were melted unissued.

Most collectors would envision the ideal coin collection as one in which the specimens showed no trace of either tarnish or wear and, indeed, such a new and perfect coin is desirable and beautiful to behold. Yet many earlier dates prove virtually unobtainable in such state of preservation, and collectors are prepared to compromise by accepting coins showing a fair degree of legitimate wear. The grading of circulated coins is a delicate art, and even experts may not be in full agreement, but a number of standards of "condition" have come to win fairly general acceptance.

Proof coins are in a category by themselves, for these medallic gems are struck on specially prepared blanks from polished dies, for presentation purposes or for collectors, and normally are available only at a premium price. Canada does not normally strike proof coins, but has done so in a number of key years, including 1858, 1870, 1902, 1908, 1911 and 1937. The Royal Canadian Mint does, however, select choice specimens of its regular strikings, and afford them special handling. These "proof-like" coins have a minimum of the nicks, scratches and bruises associated with bag-shipped coinage, and are popular with collectors. Information regarding the ordering of a set of coinage of the current year (six coins, cent through dollar) may be obtained by writing to Coins Uncirculated, P.O. Box 470, Ottawa 2, Canada.

Decimal series of Canada, as would be expected, include a number of interesting types and varieties, meriting special mention. The cataloguer has recorded a number of these in a listing which follows these introductory words.

Canada has witnessed step by step changes in her monetary tradition, starting with carved beads of purple and white shell *wampum* (which the European counterfeited); followed by "made beaver," or prepared beaver pelt, a long-term unit of reckoning (note the Hudson's Bay tokens in this denomination); somewhat later providing a proud gold and silver coinage along with an ornate bank currency; until finally, today — when monetary gold and local bank bills have vanished, we have a central bank and a token subsidiary coinage to supply the nation's cash.

Fineness of Canadian five dollar and ten dollar gold coins is .900, and the Canadian sovereign .916⅔.

Fineness of Canadian silver coins 1858 to 1919, .925; 1920 to date, .800.

These are the names corresponding to certain initials that are found on the Canadian decimal series and some tokens.

S.T. — Stephen Trenka	E.H. — Emmanuel Hahn
T.S. — Thomas Shingles	P.M. — Percy Metcalfe
M.G. — (Mrs.) Mary Gillick	L.C.W., or L.W. — Leonard C. Wyon
B.M. — (Sir) Bertram MacKennal	W.W. — William Wyon
H.P. — Humphrey Paget	B.P. — Benedetto Pistrucci
D.E.S. — G. W. DeSaulles	T.B. — Thomas Brock
K.G. — Kruger Gray	J.E.B. — (Sir) Joachim E. Boehm

Canadian Commemoratives

Commemorative money is a tradition dating back to ancient Greece and Rome. Coins which commemorate great events and their anniversaries provide one of the most interesting facets of numismatics. This century has seen a good number of significant commemorative issues, and the United States has contributed richly to the series. Canada offers five commemorative coins, and one distinctive bank note. The coins are attractive, and Canada's policy of issuing them makes it possible for them to have a place in every collection.

In the United States the popular commemorative half dollars and their silver and gold counterparts have been released at a premium, to raise funds for special purposes, and have been strictly limited as to quantity. Surpluses were melted, and few of these special coins ever reached circulation or functioned as money. By contrast Canada's commemoratives have replaced the regular issues of specified years, and have been released in a normal manner at face value. Canada's first silver dollar was a commemorative, marking (in 1935) the silver anniversary of the reign of King George V. The obverse inscription alludes to this commemoration. The coin was popular and many were issued. It is true that the Canadian silver dollar functions more as a presentation piece, (for birthdays, anniversaries) than as currency, but the 1935 issue was released in ample quantity to be accessible at the present time. The commemorative bank note of the same date, a $25 note portraying King George and Queen Mary and depicting Windsor Castle, also was produced in quantity, but low demand kept the notes from reaching circulation and the issue is rare. The commemorative coins have invariably been popular. The 1939 dollar showed Ottawa's Parliament Buildings, and marked the royal visit of that year. Mintage set a record. The 1949 commemorative, also a silver dollar, celebrated the entry of Newfoundland into Confederation, with a splendid likeness of Cabot's ship, the Matthew. The five-cent coin of 1951, depicting a stylized nickel refinery, is a commemorative, marking the two hundredth anniversary of the isolation of the element nickel, important in Canadian economy. The latest and best known of Canada's commemoratives, the 1958 Totem Pole dollar, celebrates the centennial of the establishment of British Columbia as a crown colony, and captured the public fancy to the extent of more than doubling previous dollar mintage records. These Canadian commemoratives, therefore, are plentiful and numismatically accessible— which is fortunate, for they form good conversation pieces about which to develop a topical collection.

[7]

Coinage of Newfoundland

Newfoundland is now a province of Canada, which is added reason for interest in its private tokens and 82 years of decimal coinage. It will be noted that Prince Edward Island, Nova Scotia and New Brunswick each had official coinage prior to union with Canada, as did the Province of Canada. Token issues were extensive, but only in Newfoundland was there a time for a lengthy decimal series to exist. New Brunswick, Nova Scotia and the Province of Canada (which had been the separate colonies of Upper Canada and Lower Canada from 1791 to 1841) united to form the Dominion of Canada in 1867. Prince Edward Island joined the Confederation in 1873, Newfoundland in 1949. From the Northwest Territories, the Province of Manitoba was created in 1870, Alberta and Saskatchewan in 1905. The Newfoundland issues prove particularly challenging because of their low mintages, but a surprising number of the pieces have been preserved, providing a nucleus for many a collection. The two Newfoundland banks failed in 1894, with loss to depositors and note holders. The result was a certain distrust of banks and of paper money, which led to hoarding of silver coinage, especially the 50-cent denomination. Of late, new interest is being shown in the entire Newfoundland series, with choice material in exceptional demand.

Mints and Mint Marks

The mint mark is an old tradition, a symbol on a coin to denote the mint at which it was struck. Study of Canadian mint marks is simple by comparison with those of the United States or of such internationally historic coins as the Spanish dollar. Decimal coinage issued prior to 1908 was struck either at the Tower Mint, London, in which case it bears no mint mark, or at the Heaton Mint, a private mint in Birmingham with which the Royal Mint subcontracted. Coins from the Heaton Mint bear the mint mark "H." All Canadian coinage from 1908 to the present has been struck at Ottawa, and has no mint mark, with the exception of the gold Sovereign struck for Canada. These are the work of the Ottawa mint and carry the mint mark "C."

Newfoundland coinage has been struck at London, Birmingham and Ottawa. The Tower Mint coins have no mint mark, the Birmingham have the characteristic "H" and, since 1917, certain issues have been produced in Ottawa, and are distinguished by the Canadian mint mark "C."

All coins of New Brunswick and Nova Scotia were struck at the Tower Mint, and show no mint mark.

Particulars on the location of mint marks on Canadian and Newfoundland coinage are given in the cataloguer's listing of data on specific coins.

Other tiny letters appearing on some Canadian coins are the initials of the designers.

Building a Collection

Knowing what to look for in a coinage series—dates, varieties, condition— starts you on your way to building an organized, worthwhile collection. Your sources of coins will be many: your pocket change, the finds of friends and neighbours, rolls of circulated coins from the bank. You will not want to over-look the splendid year sets made available by the Royal Canadian Mint, for each current year. These sources will provide you with most of the recent coinage varieties, and a chance to find earlier 10-cent, 25-cent and 50-cent coins. The "big cents" of 1858 through 1920 and the slim silver fives which entered circulation as recently as 1921, have vanished from wallets and tills. True, many persist in old teapots, bureau drawers and other hiding places of an older generation—millions of them, and they are certainly worth acquiring when the opportunity is presented. The more common dates find their way into dealers' stocks, and are normally available, with only the choicest specimens commanding a high price. Through coin clubs and numismatic periodicals you will learn of dealers who specialize in series which interest you. Distance need be no problem, for much numismatic buying and selling is carried on by mail. The rarer items make their appearance from time to time in dealers' price lists, and auction sales. These scarce items are ever a challenge, but your first months of collecting will find you well occupied with pocket change, bank rolls, and the occasional search through a neighbour's dubious hoard.

Bank Notes Popular

The most startling monetary development of the past half-century has been the disappearance of gold as a circulating medium, and the establishment of monetary paper as the unquestioned senior form of cash. To student and collector, the bank note possesses a particular appeal, all its own. Its art draws on the graphic, rather than the medallic. The history of Canadian paper money is important, for included are a number of issues of world interest, and specimens to match the finest that modern bank note engraving has produced. The "playing card money" of 1685 to 1757 offers one of the early instances of the establishment and honouring of circulating notes in the western world. "Bons," the low-denomination merchants' scrip, notably of 1837, prove historically pleasing, and the diverse issues of "broken banks" serve to record an important chapter of Canada's economic past.

From so diverse a background evolved two forms of monetary paper, popular and accessible, and these afforded to Canada's dollar much of its present international repute. First are the notes of "chartered banks," a colourful and varied series representing the many institutions which merged to produce the ten banks of issue which circulated distinctive notes as recently as World War II. These notes never were "legal tender" (a phrase which implies an obligation of acceptance in payment of a debt), but were used universally, and were accepted out of faith in Canadian banking traditions and in the nation's strong, competitive systems of branch banks. Along side these "chartered bank notes" circulated the "legal tenders," the Dominion of Canada (Department of Finance) issues, in denominations of 25 cents, 1, 2, 4 and 5 dollars, and in higher denominations, principally for use between banks. The policy was established that the 10, 20, 50, and 100-dollar denominations were bank issues — as were most of Canada's *fives*.

The federal and bank series offer interesting varieties of issue dates, signatures and, in some cases, seals, and great specialization is possible. The three series of the Bank of Canada issues, dated 1935, 1937 and 1954, lack much of the colour and impressiveness of traditional bank notes, but these central bank releases have a number of signature and other varieties which are proving popular at the present time.

Fraternal Affiliation

As your collection grows, your collecting knowledge will need to grow with it. Association with others through club membership is thoroughly worthwhile, and you certainly will wish to consider membership in the national collectors' organizations:

The Canadian Numismatic Association,
Mrs. Louise Graham, General Secretary,
P. O. Box 313
Willowdale, Ontario.

Membership is five dollars, which includes the monthly *Canadian Numismatic Journal,* and access by mail to the Library of the Association.

The American Numismatic Association is the world's largest numismatic group, and is truly international in scope. Membership is ten dollars for the first year, and five dollars for each subsequent year. Like the C. N. A., it is a non-profit, fraternal organization. Its journal, *THE NUMISMATIST,* is considered the world's finest, and Canadian members enjoy full access to an excellent Library. Enquiries should be addressed to:

Mr. Don Sherer
Executive Secretary,
American Numismatic Association,
3520 North 7th St.,
Phoenix 14, Arizona

You will want to investigate the different types of coin albums and holders on the market, and to see that your growing collection is properly housed; careful investment in numismatic literature will pay rich dividends — and, with your collection, your circle of numismatic acquaintances will grow.

Coins relate history. Coins are history. From them can come a unique satisfaction as you study such numismatic relics and preserve them for a future generation to enjoy.

THE FRENCH REGIME IN CANADA

Of the coins listed under the French Regime, only the silver 5 and 15 sols of 1670, the 9 deniers of 1721 and 1722, and the billon "marques" and "half marques" of 1738 and afterward ever saw actual circulation. Of these the coinage of 1670 is rarest. The coppers of 1721 and 1722 saw a limited circulation, the bulk of the issue being returned to France by Governor Vaudreuil in 1726. The billon coins began in 1738 for use chiefly in France, but came to be accepted later in the colonies. They circulated in the West Indies, where they achieved a hold that could not be broken till nearly 1900. They were issued from several mints in France at various dates from 1738 to 1789. Those dated after 1760 have, of course, no relation to Canada.

THE FRENCH REGIME IN CANADA

1 (501)   1a (502)

2 (503)   3 (505)

4 (506)   4b (507)

The figures under "BR" and in parentheses are Breton numbers

	BR		V. G.	Fine	V. Fine	E. F.	Unc.
1	501	15 Sols (silver) Gloriam Regni 1670......	$1500.00	$2000.00	$2500.00	$3000.00	
1a	502	5 Sols (silver)........	100.00	125.00	150.00	175.00	250.00
2	503	20 Deniers (copper)...	500.00	800.00	1200.00	1500.00	2000.00
3	505	6 Deniers (copper)...	250.00	350.00	500.00		
3a	504	12 Deniers (copper)...	250.00	375.00	550.00		
4	506	9 Deniers 1721 H(cop.)	20.00	27.50	35.00	45.00	70.00
4a		9 Deniers 1722 H(cop.)	14.00	22.50	30.00	40.00	65.00
4b	507	9 Deniers 1721 B(cop.)	25.00	42.50	60.00	70.00	115.00

THE FRENCH REGIME IN CANADA

5 (508)   6 (509)

	BR	V. G.	Fine	V. Fine	E. F.	Unc.
5	508 Billon marque 1738 to					
	1760...............	10.00	12.00	15.00	20.00	35.00
6	509 Half marque 1738 to 1760	30.00	40.00	50.00	75.00	100.00

JETONS STRUCK FOR THE FRENCH COLONIES
IN AMERICA

These jetons are not coins, but counters, made to facilitate the reckoning of sums in the old French fractional currency. The general issue was copper. A lesser quantity was struck in silver, and a single specimen in gold was presented each year to the King.

7 (510)   8 (511)

9 (512)   10 (513)

11 (514)   12 (515)

JETONS STRUCK FOR THE FRENCH COLONIES
IN AMERICA

13 (516)   14 (517a)

15 (518)   16 (519c)

	BR	V. G.	Fine	V. Fine	E. F.	Unc.
7	510 Indian in lilies.........	15.00	20.00	25.00	30.00	45.00
7a	Same in silver..........	25.00	30.00	35.00	40.00	60.00
7b	Same but with Alligator, in copper...........	15.00	20.00	25.00	30.00	45.00
8	511 Arms, & Mercury flying over the sea.........	25.00	30.00	35.00	40.00	65.00
8a	Same in silver..........	35.00	40.00	45.00	50.00	80.00
9	512 King & Mercury; Initials C.N.R........	25.00	30.00	35.00	40.00	65.00
9a	Same in silver..........	35.00	40.00	45.00	50.00	80.00
10	513 Two hemispheres.......	20.00	25.00	30.00	35.00	55.00
10a	Same in silver..........	30.00	35.00	40.00	45.00	70.00
11	514 Beavers building dam...	15.00	20.00	25.00	30.00	45.00
11a	Same in silver..........	25.00	30.00	35.00	40.00	60.00
12	515 Argonauts' vessel.......	15.00	20.00	25.00	30.00	45.00
12a	Same in silver..........	25.00	30.00	35.00	40.00	60.00
13	516 Allegorical figure and Argonauts' vessel.....	30.00	40.00	50.00	60.00	100.00
13a	Same in silver..........	40.00	50.00	60.00	70.00	110.00
14	517 Bee & hives...........	17.00	20.00	25.00	30.00	50.00
14a	Same in silver..........	25.00	30.00	40.00	50.00	70.00
15	518 Neptune & warrior.....	25.00	30.00	35.00	40.00	65.00
15a	Same in silver..........	35.00	40.00	45.00	50.00	80.00
16	519 Eagles in flight.........	15.00	20.00	25.00	30.00	50.00
16a	Same in silver..........	25.00	30.00	35.00	40.00	65.00

Modern restrikes from the original dies of Nos. 7, 8, 9, 10, 11, 12, 13 and 16 have recently become available at $30.00 for the seven in silver, and $20.00 in bronze. Nos. 8 and 13 were struck during the French Revolution, so were never used in Canada.

QUEBEC

After the American revolution, the Magdalen Islands were granted to Sir Isaac Coffin, who only once visited his American possessions; this was in 1815.

Before starting, he ordered a large number of these coins and a coining press from Sir Edward Thomason, of Birmingham. These he brought to the Islands, where the coins were distributed. It was originally intended to strike halfpennies also, but none were struck.

17 (520)

THE TOKENS OF 1837

These tokens were issued by the Bank of Montreal, La Banque du Peuple, the Quebec Bank, and the City Bank. Those of the City Bank are most plentiful. The habitant on the obverse was popularly identified with Louis Joseph Papineau, and the coins were called Papineaus for years, but there is no connection.

18a (521)   19a (522)

THE SIDE VIEW TOKENS

In 1838 the Bank of Montreal replaced the Habitant tokens with a series showing a corner, or side, view of the bank building. They were short-lived, for the manager of the bank did not like their workmanship and withdrew them. As a result they are very rare today. There is also a penny of 1839 with the name of La Banque du Peuple on the ribbon. It never circulated.

20a (523)   21 (524)

QUEBEC—THE FRONT VIEW TOKENS

In 1842, after Upper and Lower Canada were united as the Province of Canada, the Bank of Montreal was given the right to coin copper. Accordingly a new series of tokens was issued. These are the front view tokens, so called because they feature a front view of the bank. Because their workmanship was like that of the Habitant tokens, they were acceptable and issued in large quantities. Pennies and halfpennies were issued in 1842, and halfpennies again in 1844. A halfpenny of 1845 is known, but none were ever released with this date. There is a front view penny dated 1837. It is rare, different in many details from the issue of 1842, and lighter in weight. It has **CITY BANK** on the ribbon.

22 (526)   23 (527)

	BR		V. G.	Fine	V. Fine	E. F.	Unc.
17	520	Magdalen Island Penny.	8.00	13.00	20.00	25.00	60.00
18	521	Banque du Peuple Penny	2.00	4.00	6.00	9.00	25.00
18a		City Bank Penny	1.25	2.25	3.50	6.00	18.00
18b		Bk. of Montreal Penny . .	1.50	2.50	4.00	7.00	20.00
18c		Quebec Bank Penny	1.25	2.25	3.50	6.00	18.00
19	522	Banque du Peuple					
		½ Penny	1.25	2.00	3.00	5.00	15.00
19a		City Bank ½ Penny	1.00	1.50	2.00	4.00	13.00
19b		Bk. of Montreal ½ Penny	1.25	2.00	3.00	5.00	15.00
19c		Quebec Bank ½ Penny .	1.00	1.50	2.00	4.00	13.00
20a	523	Side view 1838 Penny . . .	150.00	200.00	250.00	300.00	350.00
20	523	Same dated 1839	150.00	200.00	250.00	300.00	350.00
20b	525	Banque du Peuple on					
		ribbon Penny	175.00	225.00	275.00	325.00	400.00
21	524	Side view 1839					
		½ Penny	75.00	85.00	100.00	125.00	175.00
21a		Same dated 1838	80.00	90.00	110.00	135.00	190.00
22	526	Front view 1842 Penny .	2.00	3.50	5.00	7.50	17.00
22a		Same dated 1837	60.00	70.00	80.00	90.00	115.00
23	527	Front view 1844 ½ Penny	1.00	1.25	2.00	2.75	10.00
23a		Same dated 1842	1.10	1.35	2.25	3.00	11.00

THE QUEBEC BANK TOKENS

For a while in 1852, the capital of the Province of Canada was at Quebec, and the Quebec Bank received the right to coin copper. Pennies and halfpennies were issued with the habitant obverse and a reverse depicting the arms of the city of Quebec.

THE QUEBEC BANK TOKENS

24 (528)   25 (529)

MONTREAL AND LACHINE RAILROAD TOKEN

It was found that ordinary railway tickets were not convenient for use among the Indians and workmen on the Lachine Canal, who formed the bulk of the third-class travel by this road. These tokens were therefore imported from Birmingham.

They were strung on a wire as they were collected by the conductor. The balance remaining in the hands of the Montreal and Champlain Railway Company were melted at St. Lambert in 1862.

26 (530)

MISCELLANEOUS QUEBEC TOKENS

27 (531)   28a (532)

Bust of Wellington. This token was imported as a speculation; it was struck on a very thin planchet, allowing a large margin for profit.

1830-41. Issued by James Duncan & Co. hardware merchants of Montreal.

Issued in Montreal about 1830. The side bearing the ship is the same as that of No. 166.

29 (533)

THE BRIDGE TOKENS

These are the first transportation tokens issued in Canada. They were used to pay the tolls on a series of three bridges connecting the east end of Montreal Island (the Bout de l'Isle) via Isle Bourdon to the mainland. They are sometimes called the Bout de l'Isle Tokens. The tolls varied according to whether one travelled by carriage, wagon, on horseback, or on foot. Hence the tokens are inscribed CALECHE, CHARRETTE, CHEVAL, or PERSONNE. The bridges for which these tokens were issued were destroyed by ice the following spring.

30 (534)   31 (539)

32 (540)   33 (545)

Counterfeits of these tokens exist and are known by a perfect five pointed star instead of the elongated ornament below Montreal; they are also thicker than the originals.

	BR		V. G.	Fine	V. Fine	E. F.	Unc.
24	528	Quebec Bank Penny....	1.75	2.50	4.00	6.00	18.00
25	529	Quebec Bank ½ Penny .	1.25	1.75	3.00	4.00	14.00
26	530	Montreal & Lachine					
		Railroad............	25.00	30.00	35.00	40.00	60.00
27	531	Montreal ½ Penny.....	2.00	3.00	4.00	5.00	10.00
28	532	Canada 1841 ½ Penny..	2.00	3.00	4.00	5.00	10.00
28a		Same dated 1830.......	2.00	3.00	4.00	5.00	10.00
29	533	Canada Ship ½ Penny ..	2.00	3.00	4.00	5.00	10.00
30	534	Caleche..............	65.00	75.00	85.00	100.00	125.00
30a	535	Charrette, 30b 536 Cheval, 30c 537 Personne — Same values.					
31	539	Charrette	65.00	75.00	85.00	100.00	125.00
31a	538	Caleche...............Same values.					
32	540	Cheval...............	65.00	75.00	85.00	100.00	125.00
32b	541	Personne.............Same values.					
33	545	Personne.............	65.00	75.00	85.00	100.00	125.00
33a	542	Caleche, 33b 543 Charrette, 33c 544 Cheval — Same values.					

THE "VEXATOR CANADIENSIS" TOKENS

These crude pieces were for many years believed to be satirical pieces issued as a protest against the despotic rule of Sir James Craig, governor of Lower Canada from 1807 to 1812. However, they are now thought to have been issued during the 1830's and to refer to the British government as the Tormentor of Canada. The reverse inscription, jumbled up on the coins, means, "Don't you wish you could catch them?" This alludes to the makers of the tokens.

34 (558)   34a (559)

LAUZON FERRY TOKEN

QUEBEC TOKEN

35 (560)   36 (561)

Lead. Issued by John Goudie, to be issued as tickets on the ferry steamer, "Lauzon," that ran between Quebec and Point Levis. The ferry passed into the hands of J. McKenzie, who stamped his initials J. McK. on many of the tokens. Originals are quite scarce, but counterfeits exist and have deceived many collectors.

Issued about the year 1832. Two varieties—one like illustration with "s" of Importers under the "C," the other with the "s" under the "o."

	BR		V. G.	Fine	V. Fine	E. F.	Unc
34	558	Vexator Canadinsis (Always poorly struck)...	40.00				
34a	559	Vexator Canadiensis (Always poorly struck)...	40.00				
35	560	Lauzon Ferry..........	60.00	70.00	80.00	100.00	150.00
35a		Cstpd J. McK.........	60.00	70.00	80.00	100.00	150.00
35b		Cstpd. J. T............	60.00	70.00	80.00	100.00	150.00
36	561	T. S. Brown...........	1.50	2.00	3.00	4.00	9.00

QUEBEC TOKENS

37 (562)

The firm that issued this token was one of the most enterprising in the city and is still in the brewery business.

38 (563)

This token, issued about 1828, bears the name of a firm that never existed, since the issuer's son failed to enter the partnership provided for him.

39 (564)

Owen's Ropery was set up in the eastern part of the city about 1824 and changed hands shortly afterwards. Extremely rare.

40 (565)

Issued in 1837.

42 (567)

Hunterstown is a small village on the Rivière du Loup, about 25 miles from Louiseville. These tokens were good for a halfpenny at a supply store operated by an American lumbering company known as the Hunterstown Lumbering Co.

41 (566)

This firm was established in 1849 and went out of business soon afterwards.

	BR		V. G.	Fine	V. Fine	E. F.	Unc.
37	562	Molsons (thick)	20.00	25.00	30.00	40.00	75.00
37a		Molsons (thin)	25.00	30.00	35.00	45.00	80.00
38	563	Mullins	3.00	4.50	6.00	8.00	12.00
38a		Mullins dated 1828	4.00	6.00	8.00	10.00	20.00
39	564	R. W. Owen	125.00	200.00	300.00	400.00	600.00
40	565	J. E. Shaw	1.50	2.25	3.25	4.50	10.00
41	566	Maysenholder & Bohle	25.00	30.00	40.00	50.00	90.00
42	567	Hunterstown	100.00	125.00	150.00	200.00	300.00

QUEBEC TOKENS

43a (568)

During the U. S. Civil War, there was such a shortage of small change that many merchants used postage stamps in brass frames with a mica window. The only Canadian examples are those put out by Weir and Larminie: they are found with 1, 3, 5, and 10¢ stamps.

These tokens were seized on arrival by the Montreal Customs, owing to their resemblance to the large Canadian cent. A few were obtained by collectors from friends in the Custom House during the time they were held. Various coins and tokens are found counterstamped "Devins & Bolton."

44 (569)

45 (570)

Struck in Birmingham for R. Sharpley about the year 1865.

46 (571)

Struck in Quebec for the firm whose name they bear.

Struck in Birmingham for a Montreal firm.

47 (572)

Struck in Germany about 1887. This company was established in 1852.

48 (574)

QUEBEC TOKENS

48a (574a)

49 (579)

50 (589)

Original issue in 1871 has thin planchet. Restrikes at a later date have
thick planchet. This token was struck
in copper and white metal.

Brass piece struck in Germany
about 1887 and used in a German
club on St. Catherine St.

51 (618)

51a (619)

Both of these tokens were struck in four metals: aluminum, brass, copper
and white metal.

	BR		V. G.	Fine	V. Fine	E. F.	Unc.
43	568	Weir & Larminie encased 1c Stamp....	125.00	150.00	175.00	225.00	325.00
43a		Encased 3, 5 & 10c Stamps each..........	100.00	125.00	150.00	200.00	300.00
44	569	Devins & Bolton token..	5.00	6.00	7.00	9.00	13.00
44a		Counterstamped coins and tokens..........	3.00	4.00	5.00	6.00	9.00
45	570	R. Sharpley............	4.00	5.00	6.00	7.00	11.00
46	571	Gagnon, St. Roch......	3.00	4.00	5.00	6.00	8.00
47	572	Card Token...........	3.00	4.00	6.00	8.00	12.00
48	574	Gnaedinger............	1.50	2.00	3.00	4.00	8.00
48a		Moose Head..........	3.00	4.00	5.00	6.00	10.00
49	579	Lymburner............	4.00	5.00	6.00	8.00	12.00
50	589	Gesangverein..........	1.50	2.50	3.50	4.50	6.00
51	618	St. Leon water (large)...	2.50	3.50	4.50	5.50	9.00
51a	619	St. Leon water (small)..	2.50	3.50	4.50	5.50	9.00

THE BOUQUET SOUS OF 1837

These are a series of imitations of the tokens of the Bank of Montreal and La Banque du Peuple, lighter in weight, with the value spelled correctly. Most were struck in the United States on Canadian order, but some originated in Birmingham and Montreal and one possibly in Boston. Because they are all inscribed in French, they were very popular among the French-speaking people, many of whom would accept nothing else during the Rebellion of 1837 and its aftermath. So many varieties finally appeared that they were suppressed in 1838.

52 (670)

The bouquet on this coin is the same as on Nos. 63, 67 and 68, which indicates that these were struck by the same firm in the United States as struck the Duseaman. The Belleville inscribed on this coin is in the State of New Jersey. It is classed as Canadian on account of the bouquet. Most of the specimens known were found in circulation in Canada.

53 (671)

54 (672)

55 (673)

56 (674)

	BR	V.G.	Fine	V. Fine	E.F.	Unc.
52	670 Belleville.............	3.00	5.00	7.00	9.00	15.00
53	671 J. Roy...............	6.00	8.00	10.00	12.00	18.00
54	672 ½ Penny 1837 (Only one known)	700.00				
55	673 ½ Penny.............	250.00	300.00	350.00	400.00	500.00
56	674 16 Leaves in wreath....	1.00	1.50	3.00	5.00	10.00

BOUQUET SOUS

57 (675) 58 (676)

59 (677) 60 (678)

61 (679) 62 (680)

63 (681) 64 (682)

	BR		V.G.	Fine	V. Fine	E.F.	Unc.
57	675	16 Leaves in wreath....	75.00	100.00	125.00	175.00	225.00
58	676	16 Leaves in wreath....	6.00	8.00	11.00	15.00	22.00
59	677	16 Leaves in wreath....	40.00	50.00	75.00	90.00	135.00
60	678	16 Leaves in wreath....	1.00	2.25	3.50	5.00	10.00
61	679	16 Leaves in wreath....	1.00	2.25	3.50	5.00	10.00
62	680	16 Leaves in wreath....	1.50	3.00	4.00	6.00	13.00
63	681	16 Leaves in wreath....	25.00	35.00	50.00	65.00	95.00
64	682	16 Leaves in wreath....	6.00	8.00	11.00	15.00	22.00

BOUQUET SOUS

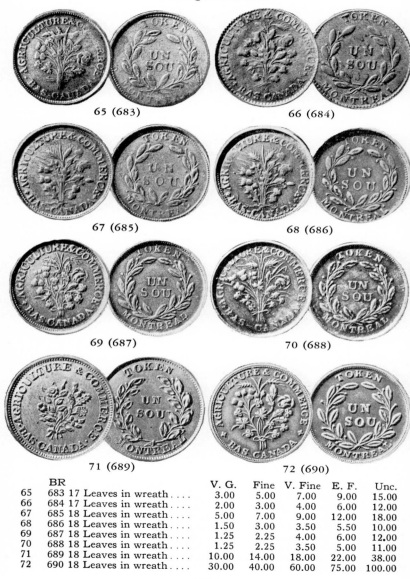

65 (683)   66 (684)

67 (685)   68 (686)

69 (687)   70 (688)

71 (689)   72 (690)

	BR		V. G.	Fine	V. Fine	E. F.	Unc.
65	683	17 Leaves in wreath	3.00	5.00	7.00	9.00	15.00
66	684	17 Leaves in wreath	2.00	3.00	4.00	6.00	12.00
67	685	18 Leaves in wreath	5.00	7.00	9.00	12.00	18.00
68	686	18 Leaves in wreath	1.50	3.00	3.50	5.50	10.00
69	687	18 Leaves in wreath	1.25	2.25	4.00	6.00	12.00
70	688	18 Leaves in wreath	1.25	2.25	3.50	5.00	11.00
71	689	18 Leaves in wreath	10.00	14.00	18.00	22.00	38.00
72	690	18 Leaves in wreath	30.00	40.00	60.00	75.00	100.00

73 (691) 74 (692)

75 (693) 76 (694)

77 (695) 78 (696)

79 (697) 80 (698)

	BR		V. G.	Fine	V. Fine	E. F.	Unc.
73	691	18 Leaves in wreath....	1.25	2.25	3.50	5.00	11.00
74	692	18 Leaves in wreath....	1.25	2.25	3.50	5.00	11.00
75	693	18 Leaves in wreath....	1.50	3.00	4.00	6.00	12.00
76	694	18 Leaves in wreath....	1.25	2.25	3.50	5.00	11.00
77	695	18 Leaves in wreath....	1.50	3.00	4.00	6.00	12.00
78	696	18 Leaves in wreath....	6.00	8.00	11.00	15.00	22.00
79	697	18 Leaves in wreath....	3.00	5.00	7.00	9.00	15.00
80	698	18 Leaves in wreath....	6.00	8.00	11.00	15.00	22.00

BOUQUET SOUS

81 (699) 82 (700)

83 (701) 84 (702)

85 (703) 86 (704)

87 (705) 88 (706)

	BR		V. G.	Fine	V. Fine	E. F.	Unc.
81	699	18 Leaves in wreath	3.00	5.00	7.00	9.00	15.00
82	700	18 Leaves in wreath	1.50	3.00	4.00	6.00	12.00
83	701	18 Leaves in wreath	6.00	8.00	11.00	15.00	22.00
84	702	18 Leaves in wreath	1.25	2.25	3.50	5.00	11.00
85	703	18 Leaves in wreath	100.00	125.00	150.00	200.00	300.00
86	704	20 Leaves in wreath	1.00	2.00	3.00	5.00	11.00
87	705	20 Leaves in wreath	1.50	3.00	4.00	6.00	12.00
88	706	32 Leaves in wreath	6.00	8.00	11.00	15.00	22.00

BOUQUET SOUS

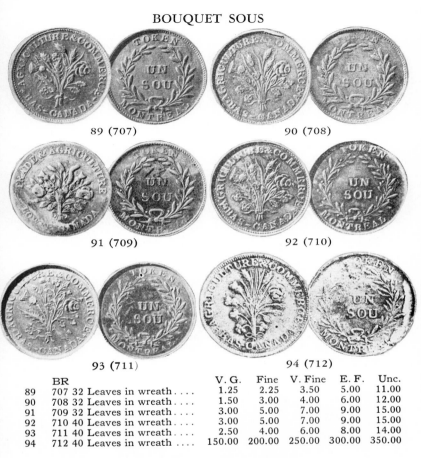

89 (707) 90 (708)

91 (709) 92 (710)

93 (711) 94 (712)

	BR	V. G.	Fine	V. Fine	E. F.	Unc.
89	707 32 Leaves in wreath....	1.25	2.25	3.50	5.00	11.00
90	708 32 Leaves in wreath....	1.50	3.00	4.00	6.00	12.00
91	709 32 Leaves in wreath....	3.00	5.00	7.00	9.00	15.00
92	710 40 Leaves in wreath....	3.00	5.00	7.00	9.00	15.00
93	711 40 Leaves in wreath....	2.50	4.00	6.00	8.00	14.00
94	712 40 Leaves in wreath	150.00	200.00	250.00	300.00	350.00

THE FIRST BANK TOKENS

In 1835 the government of Lower Canada was asked by the banks to de-
clare all lightweight and brass tokens illegal. The banks then refused to accept
any such tokens except by weight. To fill the void created by the sudden re-
moval of these pieces, the Bank of Montreal issued a token (#95), featuring a
bouquet of flowers on one side and the value in French in a wreath on the
other. The value was spelled in the plural by mistake. In 1836 the bank
was given the right to place its name on the tokens, which it promptly ex-
ercised (#96). The misspelling was retained because of the confidence of the
people in the bank's issues. In 1836 and 1837 La Banque du Peuple issued sous
of similar design with the value spelled correctly. These (#97 & 98) were also
widely circulated. The extremely rare tokens with the denomination in English
(#54 & 55) are said to have been made for the City Bank.

BOUQUET SOUS

95 (713) 96 (714)

97 (715) *98 (716)

*This is known as the rebellion token, because the accountant, sympathizing with the rebellion of 1837, the year the coin was issued, caused a small star and a liberty cap, emblems of independence, to be engraved between the leaves of the wreath.

	BR		V. G.	Fine	V. Fine	E. F.	Unc.
95	713	Un Sous bank token....	1.00	1.50	3.00	4.00	9.00
96	714	Un Sous Bank of Montreal	1.00	1.50	3.00	4.00	9.00
97	715	Banque du Peuple......	1.00	1.50	3.00	4.00	9.00
98	716	Rebellion Sou..........	1.25	2.00	4.00	5.00	10.00

ONTARIO

99 (717)

The date on this token is that of the establishment of the firm, which for many years carried on a druggist business in Toronto. Part of their warehouse was devoted to the sale of books and other forms of literature. The issue was a large one but the piece is nevertheless rare, especially in fine condition.

ONTARIO

The halfpenny was issued from 1824 to 1827 with plain edges; those with reeded edges were issued from 1828 to 1830.

100 (718)

	BR	V. G.	Fine	V. Fine	E. F.	Unc.
99	717 Lesslie 2 Pence........	25.00	35.00	50.00	70.00	110.00
100	718 Lesslie ½ Penny.......	2.00	4.00	6.00	8.00	15.00

THE ST. GEORGE TOKENS

After the burning of the Parliament Buildings at Montreal during the riots of 1849, the capital was transferred to Toronto, and the Bank of Upper Canada gained the right to coin copper. Pennies and halfpennies came out in 1850 and 1852. Further issues were released in 1854 and 1857, after the capital was fixed at Ottawa. These tokens are very plentiful. Eleven tons of them were found in the vaults of the bank in 1867 when the bank failed. They were sold as scrap metal and supposedly melted down, but the number of uncirculated specimens in the hands of collectors suggests that they did not all reach the melting pot.

101 (719)   102 (720)

	BR	V. G.	Fine	V. Fine	E. F.	Unc.
101	719 1850 Penny............	.75	1.25	1.75	2.50	7.00
101a	1850 Penny, dot between the cornucopias ..	4.00	6.00	8.00	10.00	15.00
101b	1852 Penny............	.75	1.25	1.75	3.00	8.00
101c	1854 Penny............	.75	1.25	1.75	2.50	8.00
101d	1854 Penny Crosslet 4..	3.00	4.00	6.00	8.00	15.00
101e	1857 Penny............	.75	1.25	1.75	2.50	7.00
102	720 1850 ½ Penny.........	.60	.80	1.25	2.00	6.00
102a	1852 ½ Penny.........	.60	.80	1.25	2.00	6.00
102b	1854 ½ Penny.........	.60	.80	1.25	2.00	6.00
102c	1854 ½ Penny Crosslet 4	12.00	15.00	20.00	30.00	45.00
102d	1857 ½ Penny.........	.60	.80	1.25	2.00	6.00

COPPER COMPANY OF UPPER CANADA

These pieces were never seen in Canada until about 1870. They were struck in England during the period of the eighteenth century copper tokens as a speculation by coin dealers. The story that they were struck on Governor Simcoe's orders has no foundation. Restrikes have oval O's in COPPER COMPANY; the originals have round O's.

103 (721)   104 (722)

The reverse of this token belongs to No. 103, and the obverse to one issued for Kentucky.

	BR		Unc.	Proof
103	721	Copper Co. of Up. Canada Original, has round "O" in "Copper"............................		300.00
103a		Restrike, has oval O in "Copper".............	150.00	
103b		Restrike in silver...........................	200.00	
103c		Restrike in white metal.....................	150.00	
103d		Restrike in gold............................	300.00	
103e		Restrike in aluminum.......................	150.00	
104	722	British Settlement Kentucky. Silver proof.......		———
104a		Bronze proof................................		250.00

THE BROCK TOKENS

These lightweight tokens were issued in Upper Canada in memory of General Brock, who was killed at the Battle of Queenston Heights in 1812. They were struck on the "York Shilling" standard then in use in Upper Canada, whereby the Spanish dollar was worth eight shillings currency.

105 (723)   106 (724)

	BR	V. G.	Fine	V. Fine	E. F.	Unc.
105	723 Isaac Brock Ship 1812..	2.00	3.00	4.50	7.00	14.00
106	724 Brock Monument......	1.75	2.50	4.00	6.00	12.00

THE BROCK TOKENS

This token combines the obverse of 105 and the reverse of 106.

107 (725)

ONTARIO TOKENS

About 1820, Upper Canada adopted Halifax Currency, valuing the Spanish dollar at five shillings. Accordingly the halfpennies struck in or after 1820 are heavier than the Brock tokens.

The halfpenny of 1815 (#108) is doubtless antedated to evade laws against private tokens.

108 (726)

These pieces had an extensive circulation in Upper Canada, and the number of varieties would seem to indicate that more than one business house participated in their issue.

109 (727) Five varieties

This token seems to have been issued by a wholesale grocer, and the words Upper Canada on the cask indicate that the whiskey trade was one of the first established in the province, and eventually drove rum, so popular among Canadians, out of use.

110 (728)

Probably issued by the same firm as issued No. 110. The cask inscribed Jamaica refers to the use of Jamaica Rum. This token is much rarer and is usually found with the wording on cask worn.

111 (729)

	BR	V. G.	Fine	V. Fine	E. F.	Unc.
107	725 Brock—Ship 1816	10.00	15.00	20.00	25.00	35.00
108	726 Comm. Change 1815	5.00	7.00	9.00	12.00	18.00
109	727 Crossed Shovels	1.25	2.00	3.00	4.50	9.00
110	728 Cask—Upper Canada . . .	10.00	15.00	25.00	35.00	70.00
111	729 Cask—Jamaica	75.00	100.00	125.00	150.00	250.00

ONTARIO TOKENS

Two Varieties—1823 & 1833

The bulk of the transportation trade of Upper Canada was carried on by sloops sailing on Lake Ontario. There were few large vessels. This design therefore, became very popular among importers of tokens.

112 (730)

113 (731)

This token dated 1832 bears the bust of George IV, who died two years earlier. The same mistake occurred on the Nova Scotia 1832 issue. This token is considered to be a private issue.

114 (732)

Issued by Iliffe, 170 Rideau Street, Ottawa, by whom they were used for a number of years as bread checks. Several varieties.

115 (735)   116 (736)

The Toronto "Globe," having for a number of years the largest circulation of any newspaper in Canada, commenced during the exhibition of 1879 the issue of an evening edition. This edition was continued after the closing of the exhibition. As the price was made 15 cents per dozen, these checks were issued to enable those buying their papers from newsstands to secure them at the lowest price. Eight of these checks were sold for ten cents.

Both sides are alike.

117 (755)

	BR	V. G.	Fine	V. Fine	E. F.	Unc.
112	730 Trade 1833............	2.00	3.00	4.00	6.00	10.00
112a	Same dated 1823 2 var..	2.00	3.00	4.00	6.00	10.00
113	731 Comm. Change........	2.00	3.00	4.00	5.00	9.00
114	732 Province of Up. Canada.	5.00	6.00	7.00	9.00	13.00
115	735 1 Loaf................	5.00	6.00	7.00	9.00	13.00
116	736 ½ Loaf...............	5.00	6.00	7.00	9.00	13.00
117	755 Evening Globe........	5.00	6.00	7.00	9.00	13.00

ONTARIO TOKENS

118 (767)
A Madoc, Ontario, hotel.

119 (814)
A Suburban Toronto dairy.

A saloon token from what is now Ottawa, the capital of Canada. Note earlier name.

120 (834)

	BR	V. G.	Fine	V. Fine	E. F.	Unc.
118	767 Madoc House.........	5.00	6.00	7.00	8.00	11.00
119	814 Agincourt Dairy, One					
	Quart...............	6.00	7.00	8.00	10.00	13.00
119a	815 Agincourt Dairy, One Pint	6.00	7.00	8.00	10.00	13.00
120	834 W. Cameron 3d Drink ..	7.00	9.00	11.00	13.00	16.00

THE COLONIES

121 (857)

122 (858)

	BR	V. G.	Fine	V. Fine	E. F.	Unc.	Proof
121	857 ½ Dollar........	60.00	75.00	85.00	100.00	150.00	300.00
122	858 ¼ Dollar........	3.00	5.00	7.00	9.00	18.00	50.00
122a	¼ Dollar 1822/1 .	4.00	6.00	8.00	10.00	20.00	55.00

THE COLONIES

123 (859)   124 (860)

Struck mainly for circulation in the West Indies. The subdivisions of the Spanish dollar, which were cut up to make change, are represented by these four tokens. Those dated 1820 were struck for Mauritius.

	BR		V. G.	Fine	V. Fine	E. F.	Unc.
123	859	⅛ Dollar..............	3.00	5.00	7.00	9.00	18.00
123a		⅛ Dollar 1822/1.......	6.00	8.00	10.00	15.00	25.00
124	860	1/16 Dollar...........	3.00	5.00	7.00	9.00	18.00

124b (862)

124a (861)

A pattern struck to illustrate a proposal to establish a decimal system in all the British Colonies. About 20 specimens are known, all proofs.

124a 861 Colonial 1/50 Dollar 1823   Proof 300.00
124b 862 Colonial 1/100 Dollar 1823   Proof 250.00

THE NOVA SCOTIA COINAGE

In 1817, Nova Scotia outlawed the further use of private tokens and asked the British government for permission to strike copper coins to supply the need created by the withdrawal of the old tokens. Permission was given, and the first coins came out in 1823. This was an issue of 400,000 halfpennies. An issue of 118,636 halfpennies and 217,776 pennies was released in 1824. In 1832 there was an issue of 800,000 halfpennies and 200,000 pennies. All these issues bear the bust of George IV on the obverse, notwithstanding his death two years before the third issue came out. The reverse depicts a thistle, the badge of Scotland. In 1840 there was a further issue of thistle coins with the head of Queen Victoria on the obverse. There were 300,000 halfpennies and 150,000 pennies. Another issue in the same quantity came out in 1843.

In 1856 a further issue was released in a new design. The obverse shows a diademed head of Queen Victoria, and the reverse bears a spray of trailing arbutus or mayflower, the provincial flower of Nova Scotia. There were 300,000 halfpennies and 150,000 pennies. Both the halfpenny and penny exist with the initials LCW (for L. C. Wyon) under the head, the halfpenny being very rare.

NOVA SCOTIA

125 (867)

126b (874)

THE 1382 HALFPENNY OF NOVA SCOTIA

125c (872)

Many of the varieties of the Nova Scotia half-pennies are lightweight counterfeits, which were used along with the genuine coins because of the shortage of copper. One of these counterfeits is the variety dated 1382. Very

few of these were uttered, as the forgers discovered their error and corrected the die. This piece is very rare, and bogus copies have been discovered. Genuine specimens have a flat-topped 3 in the date and are light in weight. Bogus copies show a round-topped 3 and are often made from originals, which are full weight.

	BR		V. G.	Fine	V. Fine	E. F.	Unc.
125	867	1823 ½ Penny.........	2.25	3.50	6.00	8.00	18.00
125a	869	1824 ½ Penny.........	4.00	6.00	8.00	12.00	22.00
125b	871	1832 ½ Penny.........	1.75	3.00	5.00	7.00	17.00
125c	872	1382 Erroneous date....	60.00	70.00	80.00	90.00	150.00
125d		1832/1382 Flat top 3....	8.00	12.00	16.00	20.00	30.00
125e		1832 Counterfeit ½ Penny	2.00	3.00	4.00	6.00	16.00
126	874	1840 ½ Penny Large O..	2.00	4.00	7.00	10.00	20.00
126a		1840 ½ Penny Small O..	1.75	3.50	5.00	8.00	18.00
126b		1840 ½ Penny Medium O	1.50	2.50	4.00	7.00	17.00
126c		1843 ½ Penny.........	1.50	2.50	4.00	7.00	17.00

NOVA SCOTIA

128 (868)

129 (873)

127 (876)

130 (875)

	BR		V. G.	Fine	V. Fine	E. F.	Unc.
127	876	1856 ½ Penny.........	2.00	3.00	5.00	7.00	15.00
127a		L. C. W. under bust....	35.00	40.00	50.00	60.00	90.00
128	868	1824 Penny............	4.00	6.00	8.00	12.00	20.00
128a	870	1832 Penny............	2.00	3.00	6.00	8.00	16.00
128b		Counterfeit 1832 Penny.	2.00	3.00	6.00	8.00	16.00
		(Counterfeit pennies are lighter in weight.)					
129	873	1840 Penny............	2.00	3.00	6.00	8.00	16.00
129a		1843 Penny............	5.00	7.00	9.00	12.00	22.00
130	875	1856 Penny............	2.50	4.00	7.00	9.00	18.00
130a		L. C. W. under bust....	2.00	3.00	6.00	8.00	16.00

NOVA SCOTIA DECIMAL COINAGE

Nova Scotia adopted the decimal system in 1860, issuing cents and half cents in 1861 and 1864, with a small issue of cents in 1862. It was decided to use the British silver for the time being, with the pound rated at $5. This made the sixpence worth 12½¢, which made it necessary to issue half cents.

NOVA SCOTIA DECIMAL COINAGE

V.G. — Little detail to the hair over the ear or the braid.
Fine — Strands of hair over the ear begin to merge together and the braid is worn.
V.F. — The hair over the ear is worn, the braid is clear but no longer sharp.
E.F. — Slight wear on the hair over the ear and the braid that holds the knot in place is sharp and clear.

131 (877)   132a (878)

NOVA SCOTIA MISCELLANEOUS TOKENS

133 (879)   134 (880) Known in copper and brass

The obverse of this token is the same as No. 135 and is obviously an earlier issue by the same firm.

Broke was commander of the frigate Shannon that captured the United States war vessel Chesapeake off Boston Harbour on the first of June 1813; on the 6th of June he brought his prize into the port of Halifax. As this most important naval action of the war of 1812-14 followed a number of defeats, Broke was feted during his stay in Halifax.
3 varieties.

135 (881) 2 varieties

The frigate here portrayed is intended to represent the Shannon entering the Port of Halifax. Carritt and Alport were dry-goods merchants.

BR		Quantity Minted	G.	V.G.	Fine	V.F.	E.F.	Unc.	B.U.
131	877 1861 Cent.....	800,000	1.25	1.50	2.00	4.00	6.00	15.00	40.00
131a	1862 Cent....	*1,000,000	12.00	16.00	21.00	35.00	50.00	100.00	200.00
131b	1864 Cent.....	800,000	1.35	1.60	2.25	4.25	6.50	17.00	45.00
132	878 1861 Half Cent	400,000	4.00	5.00	6.00	7.50	9.00	18.00	35.00
132a	1864 Half Cent	400,000	4.00	5.00	6.00	7.50	9.00	18.00	35.00
133	879 Broke.................			3.00	4.00	6.00	8.00	14.00	
134	880 Trade.................			5.00	7.50	10.00	13.00	20.00	
135	881 Carritt & Alport.......			2.50	3.50	5.00	8.00	14.00	

* Obviously an error in mint report. Probably 100,000.

NOVA SCOTIA

136 (882)   137 (883)
                             2 Varieties

Hosterman & Etter were hardware merchants and watchmakers. The building represented on these tokens was Government House.

138 (884)   139 (885)
2 Varieties

Both of these tokens were issued by Starr & Shannon, who were in the hardware business.

140 (886)   141 (887)

No. 140. Three varieties, differing in the appearance of the bust. Two of the busts are similar to two of the busts on Token No. 145 and another like the bust on No. 137. No. 141 similar to 140 but obverse and reverse inscriptions have been transposed.

	BR	V. G.	Fine	V. Fine	E. F.	Unc.
136	882 Hosterman & Etter.....	2.50	3.50	5.00	7.00	14.00
137	883 Hosterman & Etter.....	2.00	3.00	4.50	6.00	12.00
138	884 Starr & Shannon.......	2.00	3.00	4.50	6.00	12.00
139	885 Comm. Change........	2.50	3.50	5.00	7.00	14.00
140	886 British Copper........	2.00	3.00	4.50	6.00	12.00
141	887 British Copper........	6.00	8.00	10.00	12.00	24.00

NOVA SCOTIA

142 (888)
4 Varieties

143 (889)
2 Varieties

144 (890)

145 (891)
3 Varieties differing in the bust.

146 (892)

147 (893)

Issued by W. A. & S. Black, hardware merchants, who were sons of the Rev. Wm. Black, the founder of Methodism in Nova Scotia.

	BR		V. G.	Fine	V. Fine	E. F.	Unc.
142	888	Navig. & Trade	2.00	3.00	4.50	6.00	12.00
143	889	Halifax	2.50	3.50	5.00	7.00	14.00
144	890	M. W. White	2.50	3.50	5.00	7.00	14.00
145	891	J. A. Barry	2.00	3.00	4.50	6.00	12.00
146	892	Black's Hardware	2.00	3.00	4.50	6.00	12.00
147	893	Black's Hardware	2.50	3.50	5.00	7.00	14.00

NOVA SCOTIA

148 (894)

149 (895)

This, one of the rarest of Nova Scotian tokens, was probably issued by some politician favouring the union of Nova Scotia and New Brunswick.

150 (896)

John Brown was a West Indian merchant. This token was issued in 1815.

151 (897)

Robert Purves commenced business in 1865 and retired in 1870.

152 (899) 2 Varieties

153 (900)

Blackley for some years did a retail business at Halifax. The word "salt" seems to be an error of the Birmingham engraver, who seems to have confounded dry goods with something relating to dried codfish.

154 (901)

	BR	V. G.	Fine	V. Fine	E. F.	Unc.
148	894 Trade & Navigation....	2.50	3.50	4.50	6.00	12.00
149	895 Success..............	9.00	12.00	15.00	20.00	35.00
150	896 J. Brown.............	2.00	3.00	4.50	6.00	12.00
151	897 Purves..............	3.00	4.00	5.00	7.00	14.00
152	899 Whites..............	5.00	6.00	7.00	8.00	16.00
153	900 Ferry...............	1.50	2.00	2.25	2.50	3.50
154	901 Blakley.............	3.00	4.00	5.00	7.00	12.00
155	902 Gass' Tea...........	4.00	5.00	6.00	8.00	13.00
156	903 R.S................	8.00	10.00	15.00	20.00	30.00

NOVA SCOTIA

155 (902)   156 (903)

This token was struck in Montreal and was a small issue.

Richard Sheppard was a Halifax hotel-keeper, and this check was used in connection with the billiard room, being good for one game. Issued in 1886.

DECIMAL COINAGE OF NEW BRUNSWICK

New Brunswick adopted decimal currency in 1860, the first coins being cents in 1861. Half cents were struck and sent out by mistake, for these were never ordered by the New Brunswick government. However a few did get out into circulation. Silver five-cent, ten-cent and twenty-cent pieces were issued in 1862 and 1864, and cents again in 1864.

157 (904)   158b (905)   159a (906)

G. — Hair over ear worn through.

V.G. — No details in the hair over the ear and the jewels in the diadem are partly worn away.

Fine — Strands of the hair over the ear begin to merge together and jewels slightly blurred.

V.F. — Hair and the jewels clear but not sharp.

E.F. — Braid is slightly worn but generally sharp and clear.

	BR		Quantity Minted	G.	V.G.	Fine	V.F.	E.F.	Unc.
157	904	1862 20 Cents..	150,000	12.00	16.00	20.00	25.00	33.00	125.00
157a		1864 20 Cents..	150,000	13.00	18.00	23.00	28.00	35.00	135.00
158	905	1862 10 Cents..	150,000	20.00	27.00	37.00	55.00	75.00	200.00
158a		1862 10 Cents recut "2"	18.00	25.00	35.00	50.00	70.00	175.00
158b		1864 10 Cents..	100,000	18.00	25.00	35.00	50.00	70.00	175.00
159	906	1862 5 Cents...	100,000	20.00	35.00	45.00	60.00	80.00	185.00
159a		1864 5 Cents...	100,000	18.00	30.00	40.00	55.00	75.00	175.00

THE NEW BRUNSWICK COINAGE

160a (907)   161 (908)

G. — *Hair over ear worn through.*
V.G. — *Little detail to the hair over the ear or the braid.*
Fine — *Strands of hair over the ear begin to merge together and the braid is worn.*
V.F. — *The hair over the ear is worn, the braid is clear but no longer sharp.*
E.F. — *Slight wear on the hair over the ear and the braid that holds the knot in place is sharp and clear.*

BR	Quan. Minted	G.	V.G.	Fine	V.F.	E.F.	Unc.	B.U.
160 907 1861 Cent....	1,000,000	1.25	1.75	2.50	4.50	7.00	20.00	45.00
160a 1864 Cent....	1,000,000	1.25	1.75	2.50	4.50	7.00	20.00	45.00
161 908 1861 Half Cent *222,800		40.00	60.00	70.00	80.00	90.00	150.00	300.00

New Brunswick received the right to coin copper in 1843. An issue of 480,000 halfpennies and 480,000 pennies came out the same year. These coins were disapproved by the Colonial Office because they showed a diademed head of the Queen, which had never before been used on coinage. However, the coins remained in circulation. In 1854, an issue of 480,000 halfpennies and 480,000 pennies was released, showing the head of the Queen as used on the English coinage. The penny and halfpenny are of the same design.

164 (910)   165 (912)

162	909 1843 Penny Token.....	2.00	3.00	5.00	7.50	15.00
163	911 1854 Penny Currency...	2.50	3.50	5.50	8.00	16.00
164	910 1843 ½ Penny Token...	1.50	2.25	4.00	6.00	12.00
165	912 1854 ½ Penny Currency	1.75	2.50	4.50	6.50	13.00

166 (913)   167 (914)

Issued about 1830. The reverse is the same as No. 29.

Issued about 1855 and very rare. The firm was in business a short time.

166	913 St. John halfpenny...	9.00	12.00	14.00	16.00	24.00
167	914 McDermott.........	70.00	80.00	90.00	110.00	175.00

*None officially issued, but a few escaped into circulation.

PRINCE EDWARD ISLAND

Prince Edward Island's tokens were much lighter in weight than those of the other colonies because the local currency was worth much less in terms of sterling. The earliest tokens were the SHIPS COLONIES & COMMERCE tokens, Breton 995 & 996. The famous Breton 997 is said to have been used there, although hoards have been found in other provinces as well. The chief evidence for its being used on the Island is its weight and fabric, identical with that of the later tokens.

Local tokens came out in 1840, the rare sheaf of wheat being the first. Next came the SPEED THE PLOUGH types, followed in the 1850's by the FISHERIES AND AGRICULTURE and the SELF GOVERNMENT tokens. All these are very common.

The tree shown on the 1871 P.E.I. cent is an oak—with three oak saplings. They represent: Large oak tree—the mother country, sheltering the three countries of the Island—Kings, Queens, and Prince, designated by the three oak saplings.

Decimal coinage was introduced in 1871, the only coin being a bronze cent. The Prince Edward Island cent is unique in that it is the only coin issued anywhere in Canada with the royal title in English, and the only coin of the Heaton mint at Birmingham without the familiar H.

168 (915)

G. — Hair over ear worn through.
V.G. — No details in the hair over the ear.
Fine — Strands of hair over the ear begin to run together.
V.F. — Hair and jewels no longer sharp but clear.
E.F. — Hair over the ear is sharp and clear. Jewels in diadem must show sharply and clearly.

BR			G.	V.G.	Fine	V.F.	E.F.	Unc.	B.U.
168	915	1871 Cent........	.50	.75	1.50	3.50	7.00	50.00	125.00

169 (916)

170 (917)

Issued by James Milner of Charlottetown. Usually found in poor condition. (V. Rare)

		V. G.	Fine	V. Fine	E. F.	Unc.
169	916 Sheaf of wheat (usually poorly struck).......	65.00	80.00	100.00	125.00	200.00
170	917 Plough (hook variety) 4 varieties...........	1.00	1.50	2.75	4.00	9.00
170a	(clevis variety) 5 varieties...........	1.50	2.50	4.00	5.00	10.00

PRINCE EDWARD ISLAND

171 (918)
3 Varieties

172 (919)
3 Varieties of 1855
22 Varieties of 1857

173 (920)
4 Varieties

174 (921)
Issued in 1858

175 (922)

176 (923)

One hundred of each of these Bar or Pool checks were issued about 1892.

	BR	V. G.	Fine	V. Fine	E. F.	Unc.
171	918 Prince Edward's Island .	1.50	2.50	4.00	5.00	10.00
172	919 1855 Self Govt.........	1.50	2.50	4.00	5.00	10.00
172a	1857 Self Govt.........	1.25	2.25	3.50	4.50	9.00
173	920 1855 Cent.............	1.50	2.50	4.00	5.00	10.00
174	921 Ship..................	2.50	3.50	5.00	7.00	12.00
175	922 John Joy..............	8.00	10.00	12.00	15.00	22.00
176	923 John Joy..............	7.00	9.00	11.00	13.00	20.00

924 Anse Canot. For many years these were classed as Canadian tokens from Prince Edward Island, but research has now linked them with Guadaloupe.

NORTH WEST COMPANY

The North West Company was organized in Montreal about the year 1784. It carried on operations until about 1821 from the district South and West of Hudson Bay as far as the Pacific Coast. This token was good for a beaver skin and is very rare.

177 (925)

HUDSON'S BAY COMPANY

Brass tokens, issued about the year 1854, for use in those portions of the Hudson's Bay Company's territories lying east of Hudson's Bay. These were designated by the Company as the East Main area. The name has now been changed officially to "Eastmain." The initials "N B" should have been "M B," signifying "Made Beaver," meaning a prepared beaver skin, then the accepted H. B. Co. trading unit.

178 (926)   179 (927)

180 (928)   181 (929)

	BR	V. G.	Fine	V. Fine	E. F.	Unc.
177	925 North West Company					
	(brass)	225.00	300.00	400.00	500.00	850.00
177a	Same in copper	240.00	325.00	425.00	550.00	800.00
178	926 Hudson's Bay Co. 1					
	Made Beaver	13.00	15.00	20.00	25.00	30.00
179	927 Hudson's Bay Co. ½					
	Made Beaver	11.00	13.00	17.00	22.00	27.00
180	928 Hudson's Bay Co. ¼					
	Made Beaver	11.00	13.00	17.00	22.00	27.00
181	929 Hudson's Bay Co. ⅛					
	Made Beaver	13.00	15.00	20.00	25.00	30.00

HUDSON'S BAY COMPANY

181d

181b

181a

	BR	V. Fine	E. F.	Unc.
181a	Hudson's Bay (1946 issue) Aluminum To-kens. Large square "1" equivalent to one white fox......................	15.00	17.50	20.00
181b	Hudson's Bay Company.			
	Set of 5 - 10 - 25 - 50 - $1.00 Aluminum	15.00	17.50	20.00
181c	Hudson's Bay Company - Labrador District.			
	Set of four 1 - 5 - 10 - 20 Aluminum ...	45.00	50.00	60.00
181d	Hudson's Bay Company - St. Lawrence - Labrador District.			
	Set of four 1 - 5 - 10 - 20 Aluminum ...	45.00	50.00	60.00

NORTHWEST TERRITORIES

182 (930)
There are two mistakes in this check. The initials of the Issuer should be J.H.F. instead of I.H.F., and the letters N.W.S. for North West Settlement should be N.W.T. for Northwest Territories.

182a (931)
J. H. Fleming used these checks, which have his initials and those of the Territory correct.

184 (933)
Pick's hardware house, Chicago, where Mr. Ross purchased the cutlery and silverware for his hotel, furnished 1250 of these checks without charge.

183 (932)
Issue 100. Note early spelling of "Winnipeg."

BR

			V. G.	Fine	V. Fine	E. F.	Unc.
182	930	Comm. Hotel N.W.S. IHF One Drink.....	13.00	15.00	17.50	22.00	27.00
182a	931	Comm. Hotel N.W.T. JHF One Drink......	13.00	15.00	17.50	22.00	27.00
183	932	Tobin 1 Shave.........	15.00	20.00	25.00	30.00	40.00
183a	932a	Correct spelling of Winnipeg	15.00	20.00	25.00	30.00	40.00
184	933	Edmonton Hotel..........	15.00	20.00	25.00	30.00	40.00

BRITISH COLUMBIA

185 (934)   185a (935)
These two gold pieces were issued during the height of the gold rush in the Fraser River and Cariboo district of British Columbia. They were prepared to the order of the provincial authorities, but were disallowed by the British government. They are generally rated as patterns and are very rare.

185	934	Pattern Gold $20.00 (very rare)	7000.00
185a	935	Pattern Gold $10.00 (very rare)	7000.00
		Same in silver (very rare)	2500.00

BRITISH COLUMBIA

| 186 (936) | 187 (937) | 188 (938) |

These tokens were issued about 1887.

189 (939)

	BR	V. G.	Fine	V. Fine	E. F.	Unc.
186	936 Central Hotel 5¢........	13.00	15.00	17.50	22.00	27.00
187	937 Central Hotel 15¢.......	13.00	15.00	17.50	22.00	27.00
188	938 W. Cowan............	13.00	15.00	17.50	22.00	27.00
189	939 Hon. J. Robson........	35.00	40.00	45.00	50.00	60.00

NEWFOUNDLAND

Newfoundland in the early nineteenth century used British coppers which, however, were in short supply. In 1841 and 1846 Rutherford Bros. of St. John's and Harbour Grace issued halfpenny tokens in large quantities. There are several varieties, including forgeries in brass. During the 1840's Prince Edward Island tokens appeared in enormous numbers, and became such a nuisance that they were outlawed by the government in 1851. However they acquired such a hold that the later tokens (the 1858 ship and the 1860 Fishery Rights) were made of the same weight and fabric.

NEWFOUNDLAND

190 (952)

191 (953)

There is another variety without the date. Both exist in copper and brass.

Three varieties, in the first of which the horn of the sheep is opposite the letter H in Harbour; the second is as illustrated, and in the third variety the ribbon extends to the letter H in Rutherford.

192 (954)

193 (955)

Issued by a Newfoundland merchant.

Issued in commemoration of the revision of the fishery treaty between Great Britain and the United States. The treaty fixed the shore limits.

194 (956)

	BR	V. G.	Fine	V. Fine	E. F.	Unc.
190	952 St. John's 1841.........	1.50	3.00	4.50	7.00	14.00
190a	Same undated.........	1.25	2.50	4.00	6.00	12.00
191	953 Harbour Grace.........	1.25	2.50	4.00	6.00	12.00
192	954 1858 Ship.............	80.00	110.00	125.00	150.00	200.00
193	955 Fishery Rights.........	13.00	15.00	18.00	23.00	35.00
194	956 P. McAuslane..........	100.00	125.00	150.00	175.00	225.00

ANONYMOUS and MISCELLANEOUS TOKENS

Most of these pieces have now been ascribed to a definite location. The Tiffin tokens (#195-197) are anonymous English tokens imported to Canada by a Montreal grocer named Joseph Tiffin. Specimens in brass are counterfeits made locally. 195 (957)

196a (960)

197 (961)

Two varieties in copper and many brass counterfeits.

Eight varieties in brass which are counterfeits.

The TRADE & NAVIGATION tokens were imported into Halifax, Nova Scotia, after being withdrawn in England (#198-201).

198a (962)

199 (963)

Dated 1812, 1813, 1814. 2 varieties of 1813.

	BR		V. G.	Fine	V. Fine	E. F.	Unc.
195	957	1812 obv. & rev. Penny..	2.50	4.00	5.50	7.50	15.00
195a	958	1812 obv. only.........	2.00	3.00	4.50	7.00	14.00
195b		1813 obv. only.........	2.25	4.00	5.50	7.50	15.00
195c	959	1812 rev. only.........	1.50	2.50	4.00	6.00	12.00
195d		1813 rev. only.........	2.25	4.00	5.50	7.50	15.00
196	960	1812 Copper ½ Penny..	1.00	1.50	2.50	4.00	8.00
196a		Copper counterfeits.....	1.00	1.50	2.50	4.00	8.00
196b		Same in brass, counterfeit	1.00	1.25	2.00	3.00	6.00
197	961	1812 ½ Penny (plain)...	1.00	1.50	2.50	4.00	8.00
198	962	1812 Penny, pure copper	3.00	4.00	5.00	7.00	14.00
198a		1813 Penny, pure copper	3.00	4.00	5.00	7.00	14.00
198b		1812 Penny, pure copper	3.00	5.00	7.00	9.00	18.00
199	963	1812 Half Penny, pure cop.	1.50	2.50	3.50	5.00	10.00
199a		1813 Half Penny, pure cop.	1.50	2.50	3.50	5.00	10.00

MISCELLANEOUS TOKENS

200 (964)   201 (965)

202 (966)   203 (967)

THE WELLINGTON TOKENS

These are a series of tokens featuring the Duke of Wellington and bearing references to his victories against Napoleon. Many began as anonymous private tokens in England and were sent to Canada after being withdrawn from circulation in England. Some were issued in Canada, as the series was very popular among both English and French Canadians. The varieties issued in Canada are lighter in weight than those struck in England. The Wellington tokens circulated mostly in Lower Canada, but spread into the other colonies in the course of trade.

205 (969) 2 Varieties

	BR	V. G.	Fine	V. Fine	E. F.	Unc.
200	964 1813 Farthing, pure cop.	12.00	15.00	17.50	20.00	25.00
201	965 1813 ½ Penny ship, pure copper..............	1.50	2.00	3.00	5.00	10.00
202	966 Gen'l Accommod. ½ P. ship pure copper.....	1.50	2.50	3.50	5.50	11.00
203	967 Trade 1838 Penny......	1.50	3.00	4.00	6.00	12.00
204	968 Wellington Penny	25.00	30.00	35.00	40.00	50.00
205	969 Wellington 1813 ½ Penny	1.25	2.50	3.50	5.50	11.00

THE WELLINGTON TOKENS

206 (970)

206a

207 (971)

208 (972) 2 Varieties

209 (973)

210 (974)

	BR	V. G.	Fine	V. Fine	E. F.	Unc.
206	970 Wellington Penny......	12.00	15.00	18.00	23.00	30.00
206a	Same but obverse and reverse wreaths......	10.00	13.00	16.00	18.00	25.00
207	971 Wellington ½ P........	1.50	2.00	3.00	5.00	10.00
208	972 Wellington ½ P........	1.50	2.00	3.00	5.00	10.00
209	973 Wellington ½ P........	25.00	35.00	45.00	55.00	75.00
210	974 Wellington 1813 P......	11.00	14.00	17.00	20.00	30.00

THE WELLINGTON TOKENS

211 (975)

212 (976) 2 Varieties

213 (977)

214 (978)

215 (979) 6 Varieties

216 (980)

217a (981)

	BR	V. G.	Fine	V. Fine	E. F.	Unc.
211	975 Hibernia Penny	9.00	12.00	15.00	20.00	30.00
212	976 Hibernia ½ P.	4.00	6.00	8.00	12.00	20.00
213	977 Trade 1811 ½ P.	10.00	15.00	20.00	25.00	40.00
213a	Same, dated 1813	25.00	35.00	45.00	55.00	85.00
214	978 Commerce ½ P.	3.00	4.00	6.00	9.00	18.00
215	979 Wellington 1814 ½ P. . . .	1.50	2.00	3.00	5.00	10.00
216	980 Wellington ½ P.	2.50	3.50	4.50	6.00	12.00
217	981 Waterloo ½ P. 8 strings.	2.00	3.00	4.50	6.00	12.00
217a	10 strings in harp	2.50	3.50	5.00	7.00	14.00

THE WELLINGTON TOKENS

218 (982)   219 (983)

220 (984)   221 (985)

222 (986)   223 (987)   224 (988)

222a is spelled Ciudad   Varieties in cop., brass, silver

	BR	V. G.	Fine	V. Fine	E. F.	Unc.
218	982 Victoria Nobis ½ P....	2.00	3.00	5.00	7.00	14.00
219	983 Commerce 1812 ½ P...	3.50	5.00	7.00	9.00	17.00
220	984 Penny 1813............	6.00	8.00	12.00	15.00	20.00
221	985 Cossack Penny.........	7.00	9.00	13.00	17.00	22.00
222	986 Cuidad-Madrid Wellington Victories.........	1.25	1.50	2.50	4.00	7.00
222a	Ciudad-Madrid Victories	7.00	10.00	15.00	20.00	25.00
223	987 Cuidad-Salamanca......	1.25	1.50	2.50	4.00	8.00
223a	Same in silver..........	40.00	50.00	60.00	75.00	125.00
224	988 Salam - St. Sebastian ...	1.50	2.00	3.00	5.00	10.00

MISCELLANEOUS TOKENS

225 (989)

226 (990) 2 Varieties   227 (991)

228 (992) 3 Varieties   229 (993)

The Britannia-eagle tokens (#230) were issued in 1813 by a Boston merchant who had settled in Montreal. Lightweight specimens dated 1813, 1814, and 1815 are local imitations. The token of 1815 was once thought extremely rare, but a hoard was found in 1900.

230 (994)

	BR	V. G.	Fine	V. Fine	E. F.	Unc.
225	989 R. H. Penny............	6.00	9.00	12.00	15.00	25.00
226	990 R. H. ½ Penny (thick).	2.50	5.00	7.00	9.00	16.00
226a	R. H. ½ Penny (thin)..	3.00	6.00	8.00	10.00	17.00
227	991 R. H. Farthing.........	8 00	12.00	14.00	16.00	25.00
228	992 Trade 1825 ½ P.......	1.50	2.50	3.50	5.00	10.00
229	993 Br. Colonies ½ P......	2.50	3.50	4.50	6.00	12.00
230	994 Eagle 1815 ½ P.......	1.50	2.00	2.50	3.50	7.00
230a	Eagle 1814 ½ P........	1.75	2.50	3.50	4.50	9.00
230b	Eagle 1813 ½ P........	2.00	3.00	4.00	5.00	10.00

SHIPS COLONIES & COMMERCE

231 (995)   232 (996)

These tokens are believed to have been issued in Prince Edward Island.

There is evidence that the SHIPS COLONIES & COMMERCE tokens saw service in Prince Edward Island (#231, 233, 235, 236), but they have also been found in other parts of Canada. There are many varieties of No. 233 and it is the most common of all Canadian tokens.

233 (997) 50 Varieties

234 (998)   235 (999)

236 (1000)   237 (1001)

	BR		V. G.	Fine	V. Fine	E. F.	Unc.
231	995	Ships Colonies & Commerce	2.50	3.50	5.00	7.00	12.00
232	996	Publick Accommodation	2.50	3.50	5.00	7.00	12.00
233	997	Ships Colonies & Commerce (British flag)...	.50	.80	1.50	3.00	7.00
233a		U. S. Flag............	3.00	4.00	5.00	7.50	15.00
233b		U. S. Flag, W & B, N.Y.	5.00	7.00	9.00	12.00	20.00
234	998	Harp, Ships Colonies & Commerce..........	30.00	40.00			
235	999	Ships Colonies & Commerce	30.00	35.00	45.00	55.00	75.00
236	1000	Ships Colonies & Commerce	35.00	40.00	50.00	60.00	80.00
237	1001	Ship.................	12.00	16.00	22.00	28.00	35.00

MISCELLANEOUS TOKENS

238 (1002) Four Varieties   239 (1003)

240 (1004)   241 (1005)

3 Varieties of 1812
2 Varieties of 1815

242 (1006)   243 (1007)

2 Varieties

	BR		V. G.	Fine	V. Fine	E. F.	Unc.
238	1002	Bust, Ships Colonies & Commerce...........	2.50	3.50	4.50	6.00	12.00
238a		Broad flat rim variety ...	10.00	15.00	20.00	25.00	35.00
239	1003	Waterloo — Ship.......	2.00	3.00	4.00	6.00	12.00
240	1004	Ship 1815 ½ P. (brass and copper)....	2.00	3.00	4.00	6.00	12.00
240a		Ship 1812 ½ P. (brass and copper)....	2.00	3.00	4.00	6.00	12.00
241	1005	½ P. Ship (copper).....	3.00	4.00	5.00	7.00	14.00
241a		½ P. Ship (brass)......	3.00	4.00	5.00	7.00	14.00
242	1006	Waterloo — Bust.......	2.50	3.50	4.50	6.00	12.00
243	1007	Comm. Change........	2.00	3.00	4.50	6.00	12.00

MISCELLANEOUS TOKENS

244 (1008)
A crude and poorly struck token. Very rare.
Copper and Brass.

245 (1009)

246 (1010)
Two Varieties. Imported from Birmingham by a Toronto firm.

247 (1011)
Two Varieties in copper; one in brass.

The Bust & Harp token (#248) was struck in Ireland and sent to Lower Canada. The date on the die was altered to 1820 from 1825 because of a law forbidding the use of private tokens. Consequently the tokens of 1825 are very rare. Specimens in brass are commoner than those in copper, and are local counterfeits. The brass tokens have eight, nine, or ten strings in the harp. Originals in copper have ten strings.

248 (1012)

NORTH AMERICAN TOKEN

This token was struck in Dublin, Ireland. The obverse shows the seated figure of Hibernia facing left. The date of issue is believed to have been much later than shown on the token.

249 (1013)

	BR		V. G.	Fine	V. Fine	E. F.	Unc.
244	1008	Crude 1820 Token......	30.00				
245	1009	Pure Copper...........	2.00	3.00	4.00	6.00	12.00
246	1010	No Labour No Bread...	2.00	3.00	4.00	6.00	12.00
247	1011	Bust, 1820.............	1.50	2.00	3.00	5.00	10.00
248	1012	Harp, brass 1820.......	1.25	2.00	3.00	4.00	8.00
248a		Harp, copper 1820......	2.00	3.00	4.50	6.00	12.00
248b		Harp, copper 1825......	35.00	45.00	55.00	65.00	100.00
249	1013	North American Token 1781	8.00	15.00	17.50	25.00	35.00

MISCELLANEOUS

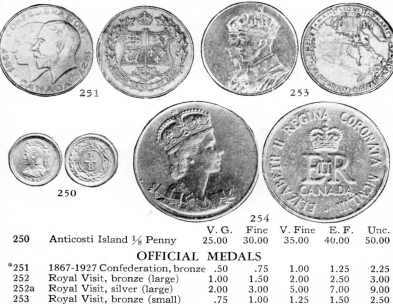

251

253

250

254

		V. G.	Fine	V. Fine	E. F.	Unc.
250	Anticosti Island ⅛ Penny	25.00	30.00	35.00	40.00	50.00

OFFICIAL MEDALS

		V. G.	Fine	V. Fine	E. F.	Unc.
*251	1867-1927 Confederation, bronze	.50	.75	1.00	1.25	2.25
252	Royal Visit, bronze (large)	1.00	1.50	2.00	2.50	3.00
252a	Royal Visit, silver (large)	2.00	3.00	5.00	7.00	9.00
253	Royal Visit, bronze (small)	.75	1.00	1.25	1.50	2.50
254	Coronation, 1953, bronze	.60	.75	1.00	1.25	1.50

PRINCE EDWARD ISLAND HOLEY DOLLAR

A thousand Spanish dollars were perforated during the administration of the tyrannical Governor Smith, and both the rings and centres countermarked. The rings passed for five shillings currency and the plugs for a shilling. They are very rare because forgeries forced their retirement from circulation the following year.

		V. G.	Fine	V. F.
Holey Dollar		800.00	1000.00	1200.00
Centre Plug		800.00	1000.00	1200.00

*Also issued in larger size in copper, silver and gold.

GENERAL VALUATIONS FOR UNLISTED
OBSOLETE LOCAL TOKENS

	V. F.	Unc.
Bakery or Dairy	1.00	2.00
Hotel or Cafe	1.50	3.00
Fare Tokens	2.00	4.00
Advertising Tokens	.50	1.00
Trading Co. Early Tokens	5.00	10.00
Communion Tokens	8.00	10.00

CONDITIONS OF COINS

The following are accepted definitions of condition classifications of coins released for general circulation:

B.U.—Brilliant Uncirculated. In new condition with full original mint lustre. May have minor bag abrasions.

Unc.—Uncirculated. In new condition, but may have minor bag abrasions. Older coins are sometimes tarnished or toned.

E.F.—Extremely Fine. Slightly circulated with only faint evidence of wear.

V.F.—Very Fine. Shows only slight wear on higher parts of design, such as circlet of coronet on Victoria issues, and of crown on King George V issues; leaves are sharp on wreathed Victoria head.

F.—Fine. More wear on higher parts than in V.F. Lower left rim of circlet (Victoria) and circlet of George V crown worn almost through. Leaves on wreathed head all show, but are not sharp.

V.G.—Very Good. Much wear, but main features of design and legend clear. Little detail in circlet (Victoria), and only part of leaves showing on wreathed head.

G.—Good. Inscriptions, dates considerably worn but legible.

The less desirable grades, About Good, Fair Plus, Fair and Poor, normally are not included in collections, except perhaps as "space fillers" for want of a better coin. Such between grades as About Uncirculated, Extra Fine, Fine Plus and About Fine, are employed by some dealers and collectors, and are self-explanatory, but such extreme preciseness of grading invites dispute.

Holed coins, and other mutilated pieces, normally are not included in a collection, though considerable interest is shown in "freaks" or "mint errors" resulting from mishaps in production. In this category are off-centre strikings, and double strikings on the same planchet.

E. F.	V. F.	Fine	V. G.

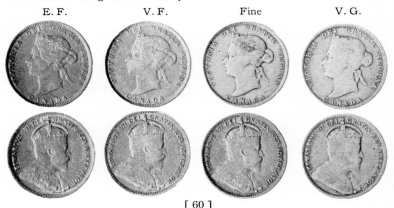

E. F.	V. F.	Fine	V. G.

COINS OF CANADA

NOTE: The 1¢, 5¢, 10¢, and 20¢ of 1858 and the cents of 1859 were issued by the Province of Canada but as they are mostly similar in appearance to the Dominion of Canada issues that followed, they are included in this listing.

Four main varieties of dates on the 1859 cents. (a) The plain narrow 9. (b) The re-engraved date which has a wide bold 9. (c) The 1859 over 58, in which the tail of the narrow figure 9 touches the upper part of the 9. (d) The 1859 over 58 in which the tail of the wide figure 9 touches the upper part of the 9.

Large Cents Victoria 1837-1901

1859 Plain, Narrow 9

G. — *Braid worn through.*
V.G. — *No details in braid around the ear.*
Fine — *Segments of braid begin to merge into one another.*
V.F. — *Braid is clear but not sharp.*
E.F. — *Braid is slightly worn but generally sharp and clear.*

Date and Mint Mark	Quantity Minted	G.	V.G.	Fine	V.F.	E.F.	Unc.	B.U.
1858	421,000	20.00	25.00	30.00	40.00	50.00	90.00	180.00

1859 Re-engraved Date, Wide 9   1859 Re-engraved Date, Narrow 9

COINS OF CANADA — Large Cents

1859 over 58, Narrow 9   1859 over 58, Wide 9

Date and Mint Mark	Quantity Minted	G.	V.G.	Fine	V.F.	E.F.	Unc.	B.U.
1859 (All kinds).....	9,579,000	.75	1.00	1.40	2.50	3.75	15.00	33.00
1859 Re-engraved Date, Wide 9 (Re-engraving is at right of Fig. "9")		9.00	12.00	18.00	23.00	30.00	60.00	120.00
1859 Re-engraved Date, Narrow 9 (Re-engraving is at left of Fig. "9")		13.00	18.00	23.00	28.00	35.00	70.00	135.00
1859 Over 58 Narrow 9......		20.00	25.00	35.00	50.00	60.00	90.00	175.00
1859 Over 58 Wide 9........		15.00	20.00	25.00	30.00	40.00	75.00	145.00

G. — Hair over ear worn through.

V.G. — No details in the hair over the ear.

Fine — Strands of hair over the ear begin to run together.

V.F. — Hair and jewels no longer sharp but clear.

E.F. — Hair over the ear is sharp and clear. Jewels in diadem must show sharply and clearly.

Date	Quantity	G.	V.G.	Fine	V.F.	E.F.	Unc.	B.U.
1876H............	4,000,000	.75	1.00	1.25	2.25	3.50	12.00	25.00
1881H............	2,000,000	1.15	1.50	2.50	4.00	7.00	14.00	30.00
1882H............	4,000,000	.75	1.00	1.25	2.25	3.25	10.00	20.00
1884............	2,500,000	.85	1.10	1.50	2.50	3.75	11.00	28.00
1886............	1,500,000	1.15	1.50	2.50	4.50	7.00	16.00	38.00
1887............	1,500,000	1.15	1.50	2.50	4.50	7.00	17.00	40.00
1888............	4,000,000	.65	.90	1.15	1.50	2.50	10.00	22.00
1890H............	1,000,000	3.50	5.00	7.00	9.00	12.00	27.00	75.00

1891 Large Date — Large Leaves

1891 Small Date—Large Leaves
Leaves close to beaded circle and vine

1891 Small Date — Small Leaves
Leaves farther from beaded circle and vine

Date and Mint Mark	Quantity Minted	G.	V.G.	Fine	V.F.	E.F.	Unc.	B.U.
1891 Lg. Date	1,452,500	3.00	4.00	5.00	7.00	9.00	20.00	75.00
1891 Sm. Date Lg. Leaves Included in above		25.00	30.00	45.00	70.00	100.00	225.00	450.00
1891 Sm. Date Sm. Leaves Included in above		20.00	25.00	40.00	60.00	90.00	200.00	400.00
1892	1,200,000	2.00	2.50	3.50	5.00	7.50	15.00	35.00
1893	2,000,000	1.00	1.50	2.50	3.50	5.00	10.00	20.00
1894	1,000,000	4.50	6.00	8.00	10.00	12.00	25.00	65.00
1895	1,200,000	2.00	2.50	3.50	5.00	7.50	15.00	35.00
1896	2,000,000	.75	1.00	1.50	2.00	3.00	9.00	20.00
1897	1,500,000	.75	1.00	1.50	2.25	3.25	10.00	22.00

Note location of "H" mint mark. On other large cents it appears under the date.

1898H	1,000,000	2.50	3.25	4.50	6.50	9.00	25.00	60.00
1899	2,400,000	.65	.90	1.25	1.75	3.00	10.00	22.00
1900	1,000,000	4.00	5.50	7.00	9.00	11.00	25.00	70.00
1900H	2,600,000	1.00	1.50	2.50	3.50	5.00	12.00	25.00
1901	4,100,000	.65	.90	1.25	1.75	3.00	9.00	20.00

COINS OF CANADA — Large Cents

Edward VII 1901-1910

1907H Cent

G. — *Band of crown worn through.*
V.G. — *Band of the crown is worn through at the highest point.*
Fine — *Jewels in the band of crown will be blurred.*
V.F. — *Band of the crown is still clear but no longer sharp.*
E.F. — *Band of the crown slightly worn but generally sharp and clear.*

Date and Mint Mark	Quantity Minted	G.	V.G.	Fine	V.F.	E.F.	Unc.	B.U.
1902	3,000,000	.80	1.10	1.50	2.25	3.50	8.00	20.00
1903	4,000,000	.75	1.00	1.35	2.00	3.00	8.00	20.00
1904	2,500,000	.85	1.25	1.75	2.50	4.00	10.00	25.00
1905	2,000.000	1.50	2.25	3.25	4.50	7.50	15.00	35.00
1906	4,100,000	.65	.90	1.25	1.75	2.50	7.00	15.00
1907	2,400,000	.90	1.25	1.75	2.50	4.00	9.00	20.00
1907H	800,000	6.50	8.00	11.00	17.00	23.00	50.00	115.00
1908	2,401,506	1.15	1.50	2.00	3.00	5.00	9.00	20.00
1909	3,973,339	.50	.75	1.00	1.50	2.50	6.00	15.00
1910	5,146,487	.45	.65	.80	1.25	2.25	6.00	13.00

George V 1910-1936

1911—The words "Dei Gratia" were omitted on the decimal coins of this year and they are therefore sometimes referred to as the Graceless or Godless coins. D. G. appeared on the sovereigns.

1911	4,663,486	.75	1.00	1.50	3.25	6.50	16.00	32.00

G. — *Band of crown worn through.*

V.G. — *Band of the crown is worn through at the highest point.*

Fine — *Jewels in the band of crown will be blurred.*

V.F. — *Band of the crown is still clear but no longer sharp.*

E.F. — *Band of the crown slightly worn but generally sharp and clear.*

1912	5,107,642	.35	.50	.75	1.25	2.50	5.00	12.00
1913	5,735,405	.35	.50	.75	1.25	2.50	5.00	12.00
1914	3,405,958	.40	.65	1.00	1.50	3.00	7.00	16.00
1915	4,932,134	.35	.55	.85	1.25	2.50	6.00	14.00
1916	11,022,367	.20	.30	.60	1.00	2.00	4.00	10.00
1917	11,899,254	.20	.30	.60	1 00	2.00	4.00	10.00
1918	12,970,798	.20	.30	.60	1.00	2.00	4.00	10.00
1919	11,279,634	.20	.30	.60	1.00	2.00	4.00	10.00
1920	6,762,247	.25	.35	.70	1.10	2.25	4.50	11.00

COINS OF CANADA — Small Cents

V.G. — Band of the crown is worn through at the highest point.

Fine — Jewels in the band of crown will be blurred.

V.F. — Band of the crown is still clear but no longer sharp.

E.F. — Band of the crown slightly worn but generally sharp and clear.

Date	Quantity Minted	V. G.	Fine	V. F.	E. F.	Unc.	B. U.
1920	15,483,923	.20	.35	.75	1.50	5.00	12.00
1921	7,601,627	.45	.65	1.50	3.00	8.00	25.00
1922	1,243,635	8.00	10.00	16.00	22.00	75.00	185.00
1923	1,019,002	14.00	17.00	25.00	45.00	125.00	275.00
1924	1,593,195	3.75	5.00	7.00	15.00	45.00	125.00
1925	1,000,622	10.00	13.00	20.00	30.00	100.00	250.00
1926	2,143,372	2.50	3.00	4.00	9.00	25.00	55.00
1927	3,553,928	1.00	1.50	2.25	4.50	15.00	38.00
1928	9,144,860	.20	.30	.75	1.25	6.00	15.00
1929	12,159,840	.15	.30	.75	1.25	5.00	15.00
1930	2,538,613	1.50	2.00	3.00	5.00	16.00	40.00
1931	3,842,776	.80	1.20	2.00	3.50	11.00	25.00
1932	21,316,190	.15	.25	.50	1.00	4.50	11.00
1933	12,079,310	.15	.25	.50	1.25	5.00	12.00
1934	7,042,358	.20	.30	.50	1.50	7.50	15.00
1935	7,526,400	.15	.25	.50	1.25	5.00	12.00
1936	8,768,769	.15	.25	.50	1.25	5.00	11.00

"The 'dot' coinage dated 1936 is actually an emergency issue of 1937, struck to cope with a shortage of 1¢, 10¢, and 25¢ pieces that came about while the new dies for King George VI were being prepared in London.

The Mint states categorically that all coins struck were immediately placed in circulation, but no satisfactory explanation of the great rarity of the two low values, as against the comparative commonness of the 25¢, has ever been suggested."

1936 with raised Dot (4 known) 678,823 Minted............B.U. 4000.00

George VI 1936-1952

V.G. — No detail in hair above the ear.

Fine — Only slight detail in hair above the ear.

V.F. — Where not worn the hair is clear but not sharp.

E.F. — Slight wear in the hair over the ear.

Date	Quantity Minted	V. G.	Fine	V. F.	E. F.	Unc.	B. U.
1937	10,040,231	.25	.40	.60	1.00	2.25	4.25
1938	18,365,608	.15	.30	.50	.85	2.00	4.25

COINS OF CANADA — Small Cents

Date	Quantity Minted	V. G.	Fine	V. F.	E. F.	Unc.	B. U.
1939	21,600,319	.10	.25	.50	.75	2.00	3.50
1940	85,740,532	.05	.15	.35	.50	1.25	2.75
1941	56,336,011	.05	.15	.50	1.00	7.00	25.00
1942	76,113,708	.05	.15	.45	.90	6.00	20.00
1943	89,111,969	.05	.15	.35	.45	1.50	2.50
1944	44,131,216	.05	.15	.50	1.00	3.00	9.00
1945	77,268,591	.05	.10	.30	.40	.80	1.50
1946	56,662,071	.05	.10	.30	.40	.80	1.50
1947	31,093,901	.05	.10	.30	.40	.80	1.50

Early in 1948 the new dies, with 'Ind: Imp:' deleted, were not ready and an emergency issue from the previous year's dies, with a tiny maple leaf as mark, had to be made of all 1948 issues until the new dies arrived late in the year.

Date	Quantity Minted	Fine	V. F.	E. F.	Unc.	B. U.
1947 Maple Leaf	43,855,448	.10	.30	.40	1.25	2.50

1948—As a result of India being given her independence, the inscription Et. Ind: Imp: ceased to appear on the coinage.

Date	Quantity Minted	Fine	V. F.	E. F.	Unc.	B. U.
1948	25,767,779	.10	.35	.75	2.00	5.00
1949	33,128,933	.10	.20	.25	1.00	1.75
1950	60,444,992	.05	.10	.20	.75	1.60
1951	80,430,379	.05	.10	.20	.75	1.90
1952	67,631,736	.05	.10	.15	.5C	1.00

Elizabeth II 1952-

Fine — Leaves worn almost through; shoulder straps indistinct.

V.F. — Leaves considerably worn; shoulder straps must be clear.

E.F. — Laurel leaves on the head somewhat worn.

Date	Quantity Minted	Fine	V. F.	E. F.	Unc.	B. U.
1953 without shoulder strap	67,806,016	.05	.10	.15	.40	1.00
1953 with shoulder strap	Included in above	2.00	3.00	4.00	20.00	40.00
1954	22,181,760	.15	.25	.50	2.00	4.00
1955	56,403,193			.15	.75	1.50
1956	78,685,535			.15	.50	1.00
1957	100,601,792				.20	.40
1958	59,385,679				.20	.45
1959	83,615,343				.10	.20
1960	75,772,775					.20
1961	139,598,404					.10
1962	227,244,069					.10
1963	279,076,334					.05
1964	484,655,322					.05

	B.U.
1965......................	.05

5 Cents Silver Victoria 1837-1901

1858 Small Date
Note space between
figures in date.

1858 Large Date
Figures in date are
larger and closer to-
gether.

G.— *Braid around ear worn through.*
V.G. — *No details in braid around the ear.*
Fine — Segments of braid begin to merge into one another.
V.F. — *Braid is clear but not sharp.*
E.F. — *Braid is slightly worn but generally sharp and clear.*

Date and Mint Mark	Quantity Minted	G.	V.G.	Fine	V.F.	E.F.	Unc.
1858 Small Date......	1,500,000	6.00	9.00	13.50	23.00	30.00	70.00
1858 Lg. Date......	Incl. above	75.00	100.00	125.00	150.00	225.00	350.00
1858 Large Date Re-engraved "8" (The second "8" in date)							
	Included in above	85.00	110.00	135.00	175.00	250.00	375.00

1870 Flat Border   1870 Raised Border

The 1870 five-cent piece is found with flat rim or border like that on the
1858 five cents, and with high wire edge.

		G.	V.G.	Fine	V.F.	E.F.	Unc.
1870 Flat Border.....	2,800,000	4.00	6.00	8.00	12.00	18.00	50.00
1870 Raised Border.	Incl. above	4.50	7.00	9.00	14.00	20.00	55.00
1871...............	1,400,000	4.00	6.00	10.00	15.00	21 00	60.00
1872H.............	2,000,000	2.00	3.00	6.00	10.00	16.00	55.00

[67]

1874 Plain 4   1874 Crosslet 4

Date and Mint Mark	Quantity Minted	G.	V.G.	Fine	V.F.	E F.	Unc.
1874H Plain 4	800,000	8.00	12.00	17.00	25.00	35.00	85.00
1874H Crosslet 4	Incl. above	4.00	6.00	8.00	14.00	24.00	70.00
1875H	1,000,000	25.00	35.00	45.00	70.00	120.00	375.00
1880H	3,000,000	1.50	2.50	3.50	7.00	14.00	45.00
1881H	1,500,000	2 25	3.25	6.00	12.00	18.00	55.00
1882H	1,000,000	2.50	3.50	6.00	12.00	20.00	60.00
1883H	600,000	5.50	8 00	16.00	25.00	40.00	95.00
1884	200,000	25.00	35.00	50.00	75.00	125.00	450.00
1885	1,000,000	2.00	3.00	6.00	11.00	18.00	65.00
1886	1,700,000	1.50	2.25	4.50	9.00	15.00	50.00
1887	500,000	4.75	7.00	12.00	20.00	30.00	100.00
1888	1,000,000	1.50	2.25	4.00	8.00	13.00	50.00
1889	1,200,000	8.50	13.00	20.00	25.00	50.00	150.00
1890H	1,000,000	1.50	2.25	4.50	9.00	15.00	45.00
1891	1,800,000	1.35	2.00	4.00	7.00	10.00	35.00
1892	860,000	2.00	3.00	5.00	8.00	12.00	45.00
1893	1,700,000	1.35	2.00	3.00	6.00	9.00	35.00
1894	500,000	6.00	9.00	13.00	17.00	25.00	55.00
1896	1,500,000	1.35	2.00	3.50	6.00	8.00	35.00
1897	1,319,283	1.35	2.00	3.50	6.00	8.00	35.00
1898	580,717	6.00	9.00	13.00	18.00	28.00	60.00
1899	3,000,000	.90	1.25	2.50	3.50	6.00	20.00

1900 Oval "O's"   1900 Round "O's"

1900 Oval O	1,800,000	1.25	1.75	3.50	5.00	7.00	25.00
1900 Round O	Incl. above	8.50	13.00	18.00	25.00	40.00	75.00
1901	2,000,000	1.00	1.50	3.00	4.50	6.00	25.00

COINS OF CANADA — 5 Cents Silver
Edward VII 1901-1910

1902 No "H"   Small "H"   Large "H"

The Royal Crown as used on the Victoria silver was also used on all varieties of the 1902 5-cent silver because the Imperial Crown die was not ready. However, the Royal Crown was not a Queen's Crown, as is commonly believed. The same type of crown was used on many British coins.

G. — Band of crown worn through.
V.G. — Band of the crown is worn through at the highest point.
Fine — Jewels in the band of crown will be blurred.
V.F. — Band of crown is still clear, no longer sharp.
E.F. — Band of the crown slightly worn but generally sharp and clear.

Date and Mint Mark	Quantity Minted	G.	V.G.	Fine	V.F.	E.F.	Unc.
1902	2,120,000	.75	1.00	1.25	1.75	3.00	7.00
1902 Large broad H	2,200,000	.75	1.00	1.25	1.75	3.00	7.00
1902 Sm. narrow H	Incl. above	6.00	9.00	12.00	15.00	20.00	30.00
1903	1,000,000	2.00	3.00	4.50	7.00	10.00	30.00
1903H	2,640,000	1.00	1.50	2.25	3.25	5.00	15.00
1904	2,400,000	1.00	1.50	2.25	3.25	5.00	15.00
1905	2,600,000	1.00	1.50	2.25	3.25	5.00	15.00
1906	3,100,000	.90	1.25	1.75	3.00	5.00	14.00
1907	5,200,000	.75	1.00	1.75	3.00	5.00	14.00
1908	1,220,524	3.50	5.00	7.00	10.00	15.00	40.00
1909	1,983,725	1.00	1.50	3.00	4.50	7.00	20.00
1910	5,850,325	.55	.80	1.00	1.50	3.25	9.00

George V 1910-1936

G. — Band of crown worn through.
V.G. — Band of crown is worn through at the highest point.
Fine — Jewels in the band of crown will be blurred.
V.F. — Band of crown is still clear, no longer sharp.
E.F. — Band of the crown slightly worn but generally sharp and clear.

1911	3,692,350	1.25	1.75	3.25	5.50	10.00	45.00
1912	5,863,170	.60	.85	1.35	2.25	3.25	9.00
1913	5,588,048	.60	.85	1.35	2.25	3.25	9.00
1914	4,202,179	.60	.85	1.35	2.25	3.25	10.00
1915	1,172,258	3.00	4.00	7.00	11.00	18.00	45.00
1916	2,481,675	1.00	1.50	2.50	3.50	5.00	14.00
1917	5,521,373	.35	.50	.80	1.25	2.50	7.00
1918	6,052,298	.35	.50	.80	1.25	2.50	7.00
1919	7,835,400	.35	.50	.80	1.25	2.50	7.00
1920	10,649,851	.40	.60	.90	1.35	2.50	7.00
*1921	2,582,495	400.00	600.00	1,000	1,500	2,000	4,000

*1921 — 2,582,495 of the 5-cent silver pieces had been struck when it was decided to use a larger nickel coin for this denomination. The silver pieces were then melted down. A few were obtained by those who ordered complete sets of coins from the mint and by visitors to the mint in 1921. Approximately 100 known.

COINS OF CANADA — 5 Cents Nickel

George V

G. — *Band of crown worn through.*

V.G. — *Band of the crown is worn through at the highest point.*

Fine — *Jewels in the band of crown will be blurred.*

V.F. — *Band of the crown is still clear but no longer sharp.*

E.F. — *Band of the crown slightly worn but generally sharp and clear.*

Date	Quantity Minted	G.	V.G.	Fine	V.F.	E.F.	Unc.
1922	4,794,119	.20	.30	1.00	2.25	7.00	32.00
1923	2,502,279	.50	.75	1.25	3.50	10.00	55.00
1924	3,105,839	.30	.50	1.00	3.00	9.00	45.00
1925	201,921	15.00	23.00	28.00	60.00	120.00	400.00

1926 Near "6"   1926 Far "6"

In the near 6 variety the top of the figure 6 nearly touches the maple leaf. In the far 6 variety it is farther away.

Date	Quantity Minted	G.	V.G.	Fine	V.F.	E.F.	Unc.
1926 Near 6	938,162	2.50	3.75	5.00	12.00	35.00	140.00
1926 Far 6	Incl. above	35.00	50.00	60.00	90.00	150.00	450.00
1927	5,285,627	.15	.25	.75	2.50	8.00	45.00
1928	4,577,712	.15	.25	.75	2.50	8.00	40.00
1929	5,611,911	.15	.25	.75	2.50	8.00	40.00
1930	3,704,673	.20	.30	.85	2.50	8.00	40.00
1931	5,100,830	.15	.25	.75	2.50	8.00	40.00
1932	3,198,566	.20	.35	.75	2.25	8.00	45.00
1933	2,597,867	.50	.75	1.00	2.75	9.00	50.00
1934	3,827,304	.15	.25	.60	2.00	8.00	40.00
1935	3,900,000	.15	.25	.60	2.00	8.00	40.00
1936	4,400,450	.15	.25	.60	2.00	8.00	40.00

George VI 1936-1952

1942 — Owing to a scarcity of nickel as a result of war requirements, only a portion of this year's issue of 5-cent pieces was struck in this metal. A change was made to an alloy of 88% copper and 12% zinc, known as tombac, and the coin was made twelve-sided to distinguish it from the bronze cent.

1943 — A new design was used for the 1943 tombac 5-cent pieces. It depicts on the reverse the letter V and a torch conjoined, emblematic of victory and sacrifice. The motto around the border, "We win when we work willingly," in International code, was intended as an incentive to the war effort. This was the first die to be wholly prepared at the Royal Canadian Mint. Collectors should beware of tombac coins that have been plated to look like uncirculated pieces.

1944 and 1945 — War demands on copper and zinc caused the discontinuance of the tombac 5-cent pieces. The coin was struck in chromium-plated steel, in the 1943 design.

COINS OF CANADA — 5 Cents Nickel

1946 — Nickel was used for the coinage of the 5-cent piece. The design reverted to that of the pre-war 5-cent piece, but the coin remained twelve-sided.

1951 — The five-cent piece commemorates the two hundredth anniversary of the isolation of the metal nickel by a Swedish chemist in 1751. A conventionalized refinery is the central motif. Late in the year, a shortage of nickel led to a change to the normal beaver design in chromium-plated steel, and this was continued until 1955 when nickel was again used for the coinage.

V.G. — *No detail in hair above the ear.*
Fine — *Only slight detail in hair above the ear.*
V.F. — *Where not worn the hair is clear but not sharp.*
E.F. — *Slight wear in the hair over the ear.*

1937-1942

1942 Tombac   1943 Tombac   1951 Nickel   1951 Steel

Date	Quantity Minted	V. G.	Fine	V. F.	E. F.	Unc.
1937 Dot	4,593,263	.25	.75	2.50	5.00	22.00
1938	3,898,974	.35	1.25	3.50	9.00	110.00
1939	5,661,123	.25	.75	2.50	6.00	55.00
1940	13,920,197	.15	.40	1.50	4.00	30.00
1941	8,681,785	.15	.40	1.50	5.00	38.00
1942	6,847,544	.15	.40	1.50	5.00	33.00
1942 Tombac Beaver	3,396,234	1.40	1.50	1.60	1.75	3.00
1943 Tombac V	24,760,256	.70	.75	.80	.85	2.25
1944 Steel V	11,532,784	.15	.30	.50	.75	2.25
1945 Steel V	18,893,216	.15	.30	.50	.75	2.25
1946 Nickel Beaver	6,952,684	.10	.35	.75	2.00	9.00
1947 Nickel Beaver	7,603,724	.10	.35	.75	2.00	9.00

1947 Maple Leaf Beaver   1947 Dot Beaver

1947 Maple Leaf Beaver 9,595,124	.10	.30	.60	1.50	10.00
1947 Dot Beaver	4.00	6.00	12.00	20.00	70.00
1948 Nickel Beaver 1,810,789	1.00	1.25	2.50	4.50	28.00
1949 Nickel Beaver 13,037,090		.15	.50	.75	5.50
1950 Nickel Beaver 11,970,520		.15	.50	.75	5.50
1951 Nickel Com'rative 9,028,507		.25	.35	.50	2.25
1951 Steel Beaver 4,313,410		.25	.50	1.00	9.00
1952 Steel Beaver 10,891,148		.15	.25	.60	4.50

A variety of the 1947 nickel has a tiny round raised dot at the lower right of figure 7. This resulted from a pit in the chromium plating on one of the dies. There is a similar variety of the 1947 twenty-five cent piece.

COINS OF CANADA — 5 Cents Nickel
Elizabeth II 1952-

V.F. — *Leaves considerably worn; shoulder straps must be clear.*
E.F. — *Laurel leaves on the head somewhat worn.*

Date and Mint Mark	Quantity Minted	V. G.	Fine	V. F.	E. F.	Unc.
1953 Steel Beaver — without shoulder strap	16,635,552			.30	.60	5.25
1953 Steel Beaver — shoulder strap	Included in above	.25	.75	1.50	11.00
1954 Steel Beaver	6,998,662	.25	.75	1.50		10.00
1955 Nickel Beaver	5,355,028			.30	.60	6.00
1956 Nickel Beaver	9,399,854			.20	.45	3.25
1957 Nickel Beaver	7,387,703			.15	.25	3.25
1958 Nickel Beaver	7,607,521			.15	.25	3.00
1959 Nickel Beaver	11,552,523			.10	.20	1.20
1960 Nickel Beaver	37,157,433					.60
1961 Nickel Beaver	47,889,051					.40
1962 Nickel Beaver	46,307,305					.35
1963 Nic. Beaver—R'nd	43,970,320					.20
1964 Nic. Beaver—R'nd	78,075,068					.15

1965						.10

10 CENTS — Victoria 1837-1901

1858

1886 Small "6"   1886 Large "6"

G. — *Braid near ear worn through.*
V.G. — *No details in braid around the ear.*
Fine — *Segments of braid begin to merge into one another.*
V.F. — *Braid is clear but not sharp.*
E.F. — *Braid is slightly worn but generally sharp and clear.*

Date and Mint Mark	Quantity Minted	G.	V.G.	Fine	V.F.	E.F.	Unc.
1858	1,250,000	5.50	8.00	14.00	20.00	35.00	125.00
1870 Narrow "0"	1,600,000	4.00	6.00	10.00	15.00	35.00	135.00
1870 Wide "0"	Incl. above	4.00	6.00	10.00	15.00	35.00	135.00
1871	800,000	5.50	8.00	15.00	23.00	40.00	160.00
1871H	1,870,000	10.00	15.00	20.00	25.00	45.00	200.00
1872H	1,000,000	25.00	35.00	60.00	100.00	150.00	375.00

COINS OF CANADA — 10 Cents

Date and Mint Mark	Quantity Minted	G.	V.G.	Fine	V.F.	E.F.	Unc.
1874H	600,000	4.00	6.00	10.00	15.00	30.00	120.00
1875H	1,000,000	50.00	75.00	125.00	225.00	375.00	950.00
1880H	1,500,000	3.50	5.00	8.00	15.00	25.00	120.00
1881H	950,000	5.00	7.00	14.00	20.00	33.00	135.00
1882H	1,000,000	3.00	4.00	7.00	14.00	24.00	120.00
1883H	300,000	10.00	15.00	25.00	60.00	115.00	325.00
1884	150,000	35.00	50.00	75.00	150.00	300.00	800.00
1885	400,000	5.50	8.00	16.00	35.00	75.00	200.00
1886 Small 6	800,000	5.50	8.00	16.00	32.00	48.00	150.00
1886 Large 6	Incl. above	5.50	8.00	16.00	32.00	48.00	150.00
1887	350,000	6.00	9.00	18.00	35.00	75.00	325.00
1888	500,000	3.00	4.00	7.00	15.00	30.00	120.00
1889	600,000	150.00	225.00	350.00	550.00	850.00	2,800
1890H	450,000	5.50	8.00	15.00	30.00	60.00	235.00

1891 10 Cents — 21 Leaves   22 Leaves
Small Leaf Missing

1891 21 Leaves	800,000	6.00	9.00	15.00	25.00	35.00	145.00
1891 21 Leaves	Incl. above	6.00	9.00	15.00	25.00	35.00	145.00
1892	520,000	3.50	5.00	10.00	20.00	30.00	125.00

1893 Flat Top "3"   Round Top "3"

1893 Flat Top 3	500,000	5.50	8.00	15.00	25.00	35.00	145.00
1893 Round Top 3	Incl. above	350.00	500.00	800.00	1,200	2,000	8,000
1894	500,000	3.25	4.50	9.00	18.00	30.00	125.00
1896	650,000	3.25	4.50	9.00	18.00	30.00	145.00
1898	720,000	3.25	4.50	9.00	18.00	30.00	125.00

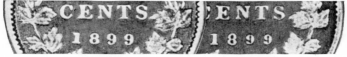

1899 large date   1899 small 9's in date

1899 Small Date	1,200,000	1.50	2.25	5.00	12.00	25.00	100.00
1899 Large Date	Incl. above	4.75	7.00	12.00	25.00	50.00	175.00
1900	1,100,000	1.25	2.25	5.00	12.00	25.00	90.00
1901	1,200,000	1.25	2.25	5.00	12.00	25.00	95.00

COINS OF CANADA — 10 Cents
Edward VII 1901-1910

G. — Band of crown worn through.
V.G. — Band of the crown is worn through at the highest point.
Fine — Jewels in the band of crown will be blurred.
V.F. — Band of the crown is still clear but no longer sharp.
E.F. — Band of the crown slightly worn but generally sharp and clear.

Date and Mint Mark	Quantity Minted	G.	V.G.	Fine	V.F.	E.F.	Unc.
1902	720,000	1.50	2.25	5.00	11.00	25.00	85.00
1902H	1,100,000	1.00	1.75	3.50	7.50	15.00	45.00
1903	500,000	3.50	5.00	10.00	20.00	35.00	100.00
1903H	1,320,000	1.00	1.75	3.00	7.50	18.00	70.00
1904	1,000,000	3.00	4.00	7.50	15.00	35.00	110.00
1905	1,000,000	1.50	2.25	5.00	12.00	30.00	85.00
1906	1,700,000	1.50	2.25	5.00	12.00	30.00	85.00
1907	2,620,000	1.00	1.50	3.50	7.00	15.00	80.00
1908	776,666	1.35	2.00	6.00	11.00	25.00	80.00

Large Leaves

Top right leaves resembling three individual leaves.

Broad Leaves

Top right leaves resembling one large leaf.

1909 Large Leaves	1,697,200	1.35	2.00	6.00	11.00	22.00	90.00
1909 Broad Leaves	Incl. above	1.75	2.50	7.00	14.00	25.00	125.00
1910	4,468,331	.60	.85	2.25	6.00	12.00	45.00

COINS OF CANADA — 10 Cents
George V 1910-1936

G. — *Band of crown worn through.*
V.G. — *Band of the crown is worn through at the highest point.*
Fine — *Jewels in the band of crown will be blurred.*
V.F. — *Band of the crown is still clear but no longer sharp.*
E.F. — *Band of the crown slightly worn but generally sharp and clear.*

Date	Quantity Minted	G.	V.G.	Fine	V.F.	E.F.	Unc.
1911	2,737,584	5.50	8.00	12.00	25.00	50.00	200.00
1912	3,235,557	.50	.75	1.25	3.50	7.00	55.00

1913 Small Leaves   Broad Leaves

Date	Quantity Minted	G.	V.G.	Fine	V.F.	E.F.	Unc.
1913 Small Leaves	3,613,937	.50	.75	1.25	3.25	7.00	45.00
1913 Broad Leaves	Incl. above	25.00	35.00	75.00	175.00	325.00	850.00
1914	2,549,811	.50	.75	1.25	3.25	7.00	45.00
1915	688,057	2.00	3.00	6.00	20.00	45.00	250.00
1916	4,218,114	.40	.60	1.25	2.50	6.00	40.00
1917	5,011,988	.35	.50	1.00	2.25	6.00	35.00
1918	5,133,602	.30	.45	.90	2.25	5.00	35.00
1919	7,877,722	.25	.40	.80	2.25	5.00	35.00
1920	6,305,345	.25	.40	.80	2.25	5.00	35.00
1921	2,469,562	.25	.40	1.00	2.50	6.00	45.00
1928	2,458,602	.25	.40	.80	2.00	5.00	35.00
1929	3,253,888	.25	.40	.80	2.00	5.00	35.00
1930	1,831,043	.25	.40	1.00	2.25	5.50	40.00
1931	2,067,421	.20	.35	.90	2.00	4.50	40.00
1932	1,154,317	.35	.50	1.25	3.00	6.00	50.00
1933	672,368	.70	1.00	2.50	5.00	10.00	55.00
1934	409,067	.85	1.25	3.00	6.00	12.00	75.00
1935	384,056	1.35	2.00	5.00	10.00	20.00	165.00
1936	2,460,871	.15	.25	.50	2.00	3.50	30.00
1936 with raised Dot	191,237 (See note page 65.) (4 Known)						4000.00

COINS OF CANADA — 10 Cents
George VI
1936-1952

V.G. — No detail in hair above the ear.
Fine — Only slight detail in hair above the ear.
V.F. — Where not worn the hair is clear but not sharp.
E.F. — Slight wear in the hair over the ear.

Date	Quantity Minted	V. G.	Fine	V. F.	E. F.	Unc.
1937	2,500,095	1.50	2.50	5.00	7.50	25.00
1938	4,197,323	.50	2.25	5.00	8.50	50.00
1939	5,501,748	.30	1.25	3.00	5.00	35.00
1940	16,526,470	.25	.60	1.00	2.50	15.00
1941	8,716,386	.25	.75	2.25	7.00	50.00
1942	10,214,011	.25	.50	1.00	2.50	25.00
1943	21,143,229	.25	.50	1.00	2.00	12.00
1944	9,383,582	.25	.50	1.00	2.00	12.00
1945	10,979,570	.25	.35	.75	1.25	9.00
1946	6,300,066	.25	.35	.75	2.00	16.00
1947	4,431,926	.30	.50	2.00	4.00	35.00
1947 Maple Leaf	9,638,793	.25	.35	.75	1.00	10.00
1948	422,741	6.00	9.00	15.00	20.00	70.00
1949	11,336,172		.25	.40	1.00	6.00
1950	17,823,075		.25	.40	1.00	5.50
1951	15,079,265		.25	.40	1.00	5.50
1952	10,474,455		.25	.40	1.00	5.50

Elizabeth II 1952-

Fine — Leaves worn almost through; shoulder straps indistinct.
V.F. — Leaves considerably worn; shoulder straps must be clear.
E.F. — Laurel leaves on the head somewhat worn.

		V.F.	E.F.		Unc.
1953 without shoulder strap	17,706,395	.25	.40	.75	4.00
1953 with shoulder strap	Included in above	.40	1.00	1.75	10.00
1954	4,493,150	.40	1.00	1.75	10.00
1955	12,237,294		.40	.70	3.00
1956	16,732,844		.25	.60	2.25

1956 10 cents with Dot

Due to a defective die a variety of the 1956 10¢ pieces occurs with a tiny raised dot below the centre of date.

1956 Dot	Included in above	1.00	1.25	1.50	2.00	6.00
1957	16,110,229			.25	.50	1.25
1958	10,621,236			.25	.50	1.50
1959	19,691,433			.15	.30	.70

COINS OF CANADA — 10 Cents

Date and Mint Mark	Quantity Minted	V. G.	Fine	V. F.	E. F.	Unc.
1960	45,446,835				.20	.45
1961	26,850,859				.20	.40
1962	41,863,335				.15	.35
1963	41,916,208					.20
1964	49,518,549					.20

1965						.15

20 CENTS—Victoria 1837-1901

G. — Braid around ear worn through.
V.G. — No details in braid around the ear.
Fine — Segments of braid begin to merge into one another.
V.F. — Braid is clear but not sharp.
E.F. — Braid is slightly worn but generally sharp and clear.

Date and Mint Mark	Quantity Minted	G.	V.G.	Fine	V.F.	E.F.	Unc.
1858	750,000	30.00	45.00	60.00	80.00	125.00	325.00

25 CENTS

G. — Hair over ear worn through.
V.G. — No details in the hair over the ear and the jewels in the diadem are partly worn away.
Fine — Strands of the hair over the ear begin to merge together and jewels slightly blurred.
V.F. — Hair and the jewels clear but not sharp.
E.F. — Hair over the ear and jewels of the diadem slightly worn, but generally sharp and clear.

1870	900,000	4.50	7.00	14.00	22.00	40.00	125.00
1871	400,000	8.00	12.00	16.00	25.00	45.00	225.00
1871H	748,000	8.00	12.00	15.00	25.00	40.00	160.00
1872H	2,240,000	1.50	2.25	4.00	10.00	20.00	125.00
1874H	1,600,000	1.50	2.25	4.00	10.00	23.00	135.00
1875H	1,000,000	80.00	115.00	215.00	425.00	700.00	1,500

1880H Narrow "0"   Wide "0"

1880H Narrow "0"	400,000	8.00	12.00	18.00	30.00	60.00	260.00
1880H Wide "0"	Incl. above	15.00	22.00	40.00	80.00	160.00	400.00
1881H	820,000	6.00	9.00	15.00	22.00	50.00	170.00

COINS OF CANADA — 25 Cents

Date and Mint Mark	Quantity Minted	G.	V.G.	Fine	V.F.	E.F.	Unc.
1882H	600,000	6.00	9.00	18.00	25.00	55.00	185.00
1883H	960,000	2.75	4.00	7.00	15.00	40.00	150.00
1885	192,000	17.00	25.00	40.00	80.00	160.00	500.00
1886	540,000	4.00	6.00	12.00	24.00	50.00	170.00
1887	100,000	15.00	20.00	30.00	60.00	140.00	450.00
1888	400,000	4.00	6.00	12.00	24.00	50.00	170.00
1889	66,324	17.00	25.00	50.00	75.00	175.00	750.00
1890H	200,000	4.50	7.00	15.00	30.00	60.00	215.00
1891	120,000	9.00	14.00	28.00	50.00	110.00	320.00
1892	510,000	3.50	5.00	10.00	20.00	50.00	165.00
1893	100,000	10.00	15.00	30.00	55.00	100.00	285.00
1894	220,000	4.00	6.00	12.00	20.00	40.00	140.00
1899	415,580	2.00	3.00	6.00	12.00	30.00	125.00
1900	1,320,000	1.00	1.50	3.00	8.00	22.00	100.00
1901	640,000	1.25	1.75	3.50	9.00	25.00	105.00

Edward VII 1901-1910

G. — Band of crown worn through.

V.G.— Band of the crown is worn through at the highest point.

Fine — Jewels in the band of crown will be blurred.

V.F. — Band of the crown is still clear but no longer sharp.

E.F. — Band of the crown slightly worn but generally sharp and clear.

1902	464,000	2.00	3.00	6.00	12.00	25.00	105.00
1902H	800,000	1.00	1.50	3.50	8.00	18.00	55.00
1903	846,150	1.35	2.00	6.00	12.00	35.00	120 00
1904	400,000	4.00	6.00	12.00	25.00	60.00	300.00
1905	800,000	1.35	2.00	5.00	10.00	40.00	190.00
1906	1,237,843	1.35	2.00	5.00	10.00	35.00	140.00
1907	2,088,000	1.35	2.00	5.00	10.00	35.00	140.00
1908	495,016	2.00	3.00	7.50	15.00	40.00	135.00
1909	1,335,929	1.35	2.00	5.00	10.00	45.00	190.00
1910	3,577,569	1.00	1.50	4.00	8.00	25.00	90.00

George V 1910-1936

G. — Band of crown worn through.

V.G.— Band of the crown is worn through at the highest point.

Fine — Jewels in the band of crown will be blurred.

V.F. — Band of the crown is still clear but no longer sharp.

E.F. — Band of the crown slightly worn but generally sharp and clear.

1911	1,721,341	6.00	9.00	18.00	40.00	115.00	350.00
1912	2,544,199	.85	1.25	2.50	7.00	18.00	95.00
1913	2,213,595	.85	1.25	2.50	7.00	18.00	95.00
1914	1,215,397	1.00	1.50	3.00	8.00	22.00	105.00
1915	242,382	2.75	4.00	12.00	45.00	115.00	425.00
1916	1,462,566	1.00	1.50	3.00	6.00	15.00	70.00

COINS OF CANADA—25 Cents

Date	Quantity Minted	G.	V.G.	Fine	V.F.	E.F.	Unc.
1917	3,365,644	.75	1.00	2.00	5.00	10.00	55.00
1918	4,175,649	.75	1.00	2.00	5.00	10.00	55.00
1919	5,852,262	.75	1.00	2.00	5.00	10.00	55.00
1920	1,975,278	.85	1.25	2.50	6.00	12.00	65.00
1921	597,337	3.50	5.00	10.00	27.00	65.00	325.00
1927	468,096	5.00	8.00	17.00	50.00	110.00	425.00
1928	2,114,178	.50	.75	1.50	4.00	8.00	50.00
1929	2,690,562	.50	.75	1.50	4.00	8.00	50.00
1930	968,748	.85	1.25	2.50	5.00	12.00	85.00
1931	537,815	1.00	1.50	3.50	7.00	19.00	140.00
1932	537,994	1.00	1.50	3.50	7.00	15.00	115.00
1933	421,282	1.15	1.75	4.00	8.00	16.00	80.00
1934	384,350	1.15	1.75	4.00	8.00	18.00	115.00
1935	537,772	.90	1.35	3.50	7.00	15.00	115.00
1936	972,094	.75	1.00	2.50	6.00	12.00	45.00

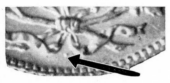

1936 with raised Dot
153,322 Minted

V. G.	9.00
Fine	18.00
V. F.	40.00
E. F.	85.00
Unc.	350.00

George VI 1936-1952

V.G. — *No detail in hair above the ear.*
Fine — *Only slight detail in hair above the ear.*
V.F. — *Where not worn hair is clear but not sharp.*
E.F. — *Slight wear in the hair over the ear.*

Date	Quantity Minted	V.G.	Fine	V.F.	E.F.	Unc.
1937	2,690,176	1.00	2.00	4.00	6.00	22.00
1938	3,149,245	1.00	2.25	4.50	7.50	45.00
1939	3,532,495	1.00	2.00	4.00	6.00	22.00
1940	9,583,650	.50	1.10	2.50	4.00	15.00
1941	6,654,672	.50	1.10	2.50	4.00	17.00
1942	6,935,871	.50	1.10	2.50	4.00	17.00
1943	13,559,575	.40	.80	1.75	2.50	11.00
1944	7,216,237	.40	.80	1.75	2.50	13.00
1945	5,296,495	.40	.65	1.50	2.25	10.00
1946	2,210,810	.50	.75	2.00	3.50	40.00
1947	1,524,554	.50	1.00	2.50	6.00	75.00

1947 Dot after figure 7		10.00	15.00	20.00	30.00	185.00
1947 Maple Leaf	4,393,938	.40	.60	1.50	2.50	10.00
1948	2,564,424	.60	1.25	3.00	7.00	35.00
1949	7,988,830	.40	.60	1.00	1.75	7.00

COINS OF CANADA — 25 Cents

Date and Mint Mark	Quantity Minted	V.G.	Fine	V.F.	E.F.	Unc.
1950	9,673,335	.40	.60	1.00	1.75	7.00
1951	8,290,719		.50	.75	1.50	6.00
1952	8,859,642		.50	.75	1.50	6.00

Elizabeth II 1952-

1953 Large Date, Wire Rim   Small Date, Flat Rim, Shoulder Strap

Fine — Leaves worn almost through; shoulder straps indistinct.
V.F. — Leaves considerably worn; shoulder straps must be clear.
E.F. — Laurel leaves on the head somewhat worn.

Date and Mint Mark	Quantity Minted	V.G.	Fine	V.F.	E.F.	Unc.
1953 Lg. Date Wire Rim	10,456,769		.50	1.25	2.00	8.00
1953 Sm. Date Flat Rim, Shoulder Strap - Included in above		.45	.75	1.50		6.00
1954	2,318,891	.50	2.00	3.00		20.00
1955	9,552,505		.75	1.50		5.25
1956	11,269,353			1.00		3.50
1957	12,770,190			.75		2.25
1958	9,336,910			.75		3.00
1959	13,503,461			.50		1.25
1960	22,835,327			.40		.75
1961	18,164,368			.35		.70
1962	29,559,266					.50
1963	21,180,652					.45
1964	36,479,343					.35

1965 .... .35

50 CENTS — Victoria
1837-1901

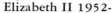

G.— Hair over ear worn through.
V.G. — No details in the hair over the ear and the jewels in the diadem are partly worn away.
Fine — Strands of the hair over the ear begin to merge together and jewels slightly blurred.
V.F. — Hair and the jewels clear but not sharp.
E.F. — Hair over the ear and jewels of the diadem slightly worn, but generally sharp and clear.

Date and Mint Mark	Quantity Minted	G.	V.G.	Fine	V.F.	E.F.	Unc.
1870 without Initials		45.00	60.00	85.00	175.00	275.00	600.00
1870 LCW under bust	450,000	8.00	12.00	20.00	40.00	100.00	375.00

[80]

COINS OF CANADA — 50 Cents

Date and Mint Mark	Quantity Minted	G.	V.G.	Fine	V.F.	E.F.	Unc.
1871	200,000	10.00	15.00	30.00	60.00	120.00	450.00
1871H	45,000	25.00	35.00	55.00	100.00	225.00	650.00
1872H	80,000	8.00	12.00	20.00	40.00	100.00	400.00
1881H	150,000	9.00	13.00	20.00	45.00	110.00	500.00
1888	60,000	30.00	45.00	80.00	150.00	250.00	850.00
1890H	20,000	135.00	200.00	400.00	800.00	1,600	5,000
1892	151,000	7.00	10.00	20.00	40.00	100.00	500.00
1894	29,036	45.00	60.00	135.00	300.00	700.00	2,500
1898	100,000	7.00	10.00	20.00	40.00	90.00	450.00
1899	50,000	17.00	25.00	50.00	100.00	225.00	850.00
1900	118,000	5.00	7.50	15.00	30.00	65.00	375.00
1901	80,000	5.50	8 00	16.00	32.00	70.00	400.00

Edward VII 1901-1910

G.— Band of crown worn through.
V.G. — Band of the crown is worn through at the highest point.
Fine — Jewels in the band of crown will be blurred.
V.F. — Band of the crown is still clear but no longer sharp.
E.F. — Band of the crown slightly worn but generally sharp and clear.

1902	120,000	4.50	7.00	14.00	30.00	60.00	275.00
1903H	140,000	5.00	7.50	15.00	35.00	70.00	375.00
1904	60,000	20.00	30.00	60.00	120.00	250.00	850.00
1905	40,000	14.00	20.00	40.00	80.00	190.00	750.00
1906	350,000	2.50	3.50	8.00	25.00	60.00	325.00
1907	300,000	2.50	3.50	8.00	25.00	60.00	325.00
1908	128,119	3.00	4.50	12.00	30.00	65.00	300.00
1909	203,118	2.00	3.00	8.00	25.00	65.00	375.00
1910	649,521	1.50	2.50	6.00	16.00	45.00	235.00

George V 1910-1936

G. — Band of crown worn through.
V.G. — Band of the crown is worn through at the highest point.
Fine — Jewels in the band of crown will be blurred.
V.F. — Band of the crown is still clear but no longer sharp.
E.F. — Band of crown slightly worn but generally sharp and clear.

1911	209,972	7.00	10.00	30.00	140.00	350.00	950.00
1912	285,867	2.00	3.00	6.00	20.00	60.00	400.00
1913	265,889	2.00	3.00	6.00	20.00	60.00	350.00
1914	160,128	3.00	4.00	8.00	25.00	75.00	475.00
1916	459,070	1.25	2.00	4.00	10.00	35.00	250.00
1917	752,213	1.00	1.50	3.00	9.00	30.00	225.00
1918	854,989	1.00	1.50	3.00	9.00	30.00	225.00
1919	1,113,429	1.00	1.50	3.00	9.00	30.00	225.00
1920	584,691	1.15	1.75	3.50	10.00	32.00	235.00
1921	206,398	2,300	3,300	4,000	5,000	6,000	12,000

Most were melted owing to lack of demand. Only about 50 known.

Date and Mint Mark	Quantity Minted	G.	V.G.	Fine	V.F.	E.F.	Unc.
1929	228,328	1.00	1.50	3.00	8.00	20.00	235.00
1931	57,581	7.00	10.00	15.00	22.00	75.00	425.00
1932	19,213	25.00	40.00	60.00	120.00	325.00	800.00
1934	39,539	10.00	15.00	20.00	30.00	100.00	500.00
1936	38,550	10.00	15.00	20.00	30.00	80.00	300.00

George VI 1936-1952

V.G. — *No detail in hair above the ear.*

Fine — *Only slight detail in hair above the ear.*

V.F. — *Where not worn the hair is clear but not sharp.*

E.F. — *Slight wear in the hair over the ear.*

Date	Quantity Minted	V.G.	Fine	V.F.	E.F.	Unc.
1937	192,016	2.50	3.50	5.00	8.00	30.00
1938	192,018	3.00	4.50	9.00	40.00	210.00
1939	287,976	2.25	3.00	4.50	7.00	30.00
1940	1,996,566	1.00	1.50	2.50	3.50	16.00
1941	1,714,874	1.00	1.50	2.50	3.50	17.00
1942	1,974,165	.75	1.25	2.00	3.00	17.00
1943	3,109,583	.75	1.25	2.00	3.00	15.00
1944	2,460,205	.75	1.25	2.00	3.00	15.00
1945	1,959,528		.75	1.50	3.00	14.00
1946	950,235		.75	1.50	3.00	45.00
1946 Design in centre of 6 ....Included in above		10.00	15.00	20.00	30.00	170.00

Straight 7, Points to Left

1946 Design in Centre of 6

Curved 7, Points to Right

Maple Leaf, Straight 7, Points to Left

Maple Leaf, Curved 7, Points to Right

		V.G.	Fine	V.F.	E.F.	Unc.
1947 Straight 7 points to left	424,885	1.50	2.50	4.50	8.00	55.00
1947 Curve 7 points to right...Included in above		1.50	2.25	4.00	7.00	50.00

Date	Quantity Minted	V. G.	Fine	V. F.	E F.	Unc.
1947 Maple Leaf Straight 7 Points to Left 38,433		18.00	23.00	30.00	35.00	95.00
1947 Maple Leaf Curved 7, Points to Right . . Included in above		275.00	325.00	425.00	625.00	850.00
1948 37,784		20.00	25.00	30.00	40.00	100.00
1949 858,991			.75	1.50	2.50	10.00
1949 Hoof over 9 . . . . . Incl. above		2.50	3.00	6.00	10.00	90.00
1950 No Design in 0 2,384,179		4.00	5.00	7.00	11.00	75.00

1950
Design in 0

1949 Hoof over 9

1950 Design in 0 . . . . . Incl. above	.75	1.00	1.75	9.00
1951 2,421,730	.75	1.00	1.75	7.00
1952 2,596,465	.75	1.00	1.75	6.00

There are many freak or mint error 50 cent pieces of George VI resulting from cracked or broken dies similar to those listed but too numerous and unimportant to list in a standard catalogue.

Elizabeth II 1952-

Small Date

Large Date

Fine — Leaves worn almost through; shoulder straps indistinct.
V.F. — Leaves considerably worn; shoulder straps must show.
E.F. — Laurel leaves on the head somewhat worn.

1953 Small Date 1,630,429	1.00	1.25	2.00	8.00
1953 Large Date Shoulder Strap. Incl. above	1.25	2.00	3.00	13.00
1954 506,305	1.25	2.00	3.00	20.00
1955 753,511	1.00	1.25	2.50	10.00
1956 1,379,499		1.00	1.75	5.00
1957 2,171,689		.75	1.50	3.50
1958 2,957,266			1.25	3.25

The design of the Armorial Bearings of Canada, in use since 1937, was re-designed by Mr. T. Shingles, Chief Engraver of the Royal Canadian Mint in 1959. The original design was by Mr. Kruger Gray. The new obverse design was first used in 1965.

Date	Quantity Minted	E.F.	Unc.
1959	3,095,535	1.00	2.25
1960	3,488,897		1.50
1961	3,584,417		1.25
1962	5,208,030		1.00
1963	8,348,871		.80
1964	9,377,676		.70
1965			.65

SILVER DOLLARS — George V 1910-1936

V.G. — *Band of the crown is worn through at the highest point.*
Fine — *Jewels in the band of crown will be blurred.*
V.F. — *Band of the crown still clear but no longer sharp.*
E.F. — *Band of the crown slightly worn but generally sharp and clear.*

Date	Quantity Minted	V. G.	Fine	V. F.	E. F.	Unc.
1935	428,707	7.50	10.00	12.00	17.00	45.00

The first Canadian silver dollar was struck in this year, and commemorated the twenty-fifth year of the reign of King George V.

Date	Quantity Minted	V. G.	Fine	V. F.	E. F.	Unc.
1936	306,100	6.00	8.00	11.00	15.00	40.00

COINS OF CANADA — Silver Dollars
George VI 1936-1952

1939 Reverse

The 1939 silver dollar commemorates the visit of King George VI and Queen Elizabeth. The reverse shows the centre block of the Parliament Buildings.

Date	Quantity Minted	V. G.	Fine	V. F.	E. F.	Unc.
1937	241,002	5.00	6.00	8.00	10.00	30.00
1938	90,304	10.00	12.00	14.00	18.00	50.00
1939	1,363,816	4.00	5.00	7.00	9.00	25.00
No silver dollars were struck during the war years 1940-44.						
1945	38,391	25.00	35.00	40.00	50.00	80.00
1946	93,055	7.00	9.00	12.00	15.00	35.00

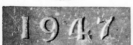  

Blunt 7	Pointed 7	Maple Leaf

		V.G.	Fine	V.F.	E.F.	Unc.
1947 Blunt 7	65,595	20.00	25.00	30.00	35.00	55.00
1947 Pointed 7	Incl. above	75.00	100.00	125.00	150.00	225.00
1947 Maple Leaf	21,135	70.00	85.00	110.00	125.00	175.00

COINS OF CANADA — Silver Dollars

V.G. — *No detail in hair above the ear.*

Fine — *Only slight detail in hair above the ear.*

V.F. — *Where not worn the hair is clear but not sharp.*

E.F. — *Slight wear in the hair over the ear.*

ET IND: IMP.
Omitted

Date	Quantity Minted	V. G.	Fine	V. F.	E. F.	Unc.
1948	18,780	125.00	150.00	175.00	200.00	300.00

1949 — To commemorate the entry of Newfoundland into Confederation, the silver dollar depicts, "Matthew," the ship of John Cabot.

Date	Quantity	V.G.	Fine	V.F.	Unc.
1949	672,218	7.00	9.00	11.00	25.00
1950	261,002	4.00	5.00	6.00	17.00
1950 Arnprior type	Incl. above	30.00	40.00	50.00	75.00
1951	416,395	3.50	4.50	5.50	17.00
1952 Water Lines	406,148	3.50	4.50	5.50	16.00
1952 No Water Lines	Incl. above	6.00	8.00	10.00	25.00

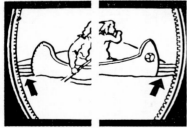

1952 Water Lines   1952 No Water Lines

1952 — Later issues of the dollar show no water lines at either side of the canoe. In the course of finishing the die, these lines were accidentally eliminated by polishing.

[86]

COINS OF CANADA — Silver Dollars
Elizabeth II 1952-

1953-1963

1965-

1953 Wire Edge   1953 Flat Border

Fine — Leaves worn almost through.
V. F. — Leaves considerably worn.
E. F. — Laurel leaves on the head somewhat worn.

Date	Quantity Minted	V. G.	Fine	V. F.	E. F.	Unc.
1953 Wire Edge	1,074,578		2.50	3.00	4.00	11.00
1953 Flat Border Shoulder Strap Incl. above			2.50	3.00	4.00	11.00
1954	246,606		4.00	5.00	7.00	18.00
1955	268,105		4.00	5.00	7.00	18.00
1955 Arnprior Variety Incl. above			40.00	50.00	60.00	85.00

1950 and 1955 Arnprior Variety   1957 One Water Line (at right)

1955 — In December 1955, the Royal Canadian Mint made up an order of 2000 silver dollars which was obtained by a firm in Arnprior, Ontario, after the regular issue of these coins had been officially completed for that year. This issue of dollars has only one and a half, or less, of the water lines in front of the canoe, instead of the usual three lines. A small quantity of similar dollars, but in proof-like condition, were issued late in the year in the sets of coins purchased from the Mint.

1957—Early issues of the dollar show only one water line at front of canoe.

1956	209,092	5.00	6.00	8.00	20.00
1957	496,389	2.50	3.00	4.00	8.00
1957-1 Water Line	Incl. above	6.00	8.00	10.00	20.00

COINS OF CANADA — Silver Dollars

British Columbia Commemorative
(Totem Pole)

Charlottetown
Commemorative

Date	Quantity Minted	V. F.	E. F.	Unc.
1958 Totem Pole	3,039,630	3.00	4.50	9.00
1959 Canoe type	1,443,502	1.75	2.00	5.00
1960	1,420,486	1.50	2.00	4.50
1961	1,262,231	1.50	1.75	4.25
1962	1,884,789	1.50	1.75	3.00
1963	4,179,981		1.75	2.00
1964 Charlottetown - Quebec	7,296,832		1.75	2.00
1965				1.75

5 DOLLARS GOLD — George V 1910-1936

Fine — Jewels in the band of crown will be blurred.
V.F. — Band of the crown is still clear but no longer sharp.
E.F. — Band of the crown slightly worn but generally sharp and clear.

Date	Quantity Minted	Fine	V. F.	E. F.	Unc.
1912	165,680	35.00	40.00	50.00	60.00
1913	98,832	40.00	50.00	60.00	75.00
1914	31,122	200.00	225.00	250.00	325.00

10 DOLLARS GOLD

1912	74,759	90.00	115.00	125.00	150.00
1913	149,232	100.00	125.00	135.00	175.00
1914	140,068	125.00	140.00	160.00	200.00

SOVEREIGNS — Edward VII 1901-1910

Fine — Little detail to the hair and beard.
V.F. — Wear spreads nearer the ear from both points.
E.F. — Slight wear on beard and hair above the ear.

Date and Mint Mark	Quantity Minted	Fine	V. F.	E. F.	Unc.
1908C	.636	500.00	600.00	700.00	900.00
1909C	16,273	60.00	70.00	80.00	100.00
1910C	28,012	60.00	70.00	80.00	100.00

George V 1910-1936

Fine — Little detail in the hair above the ear and beard is considerably worn.

V.F. — Wear on the head spreads nearer the ear and slight wear develops on the beard.

E.F. — Hair over the ear is only slightly worn. Beard is still sharp.

1911C	256,946	14.00	15.00	17.50	20.00
1913C	3,715	500.00	600.00	700.00	900.00
1914C	14,891	65.00	75.00	85.00	110.00
1916C	6,111	Extremely Rare			
1917C	58,845	18.00	20.00	22.00	25.00
1918C	106,516	18.00	20.00	22.00	25.00
1919C	135,889	20.00	22.00	24.00	26.00

SPECIMEN SETS

DATE COIN	SPECIMEN SETS
1858 Victoria 1¢, 5¢, 10¢, 20¢	4000.00
1870 Victoria 5¢, 10¢, 25¢, 50¢	8000.00
1902 Edward VII 1¢, 5¢, 10¢, 25¢, 50¢	6000.00

The following sets are in leather-covered presentation cases.

1908 Edward VII 1¢, 5¢, 10¢, 25¢, 50¢	1000.00
1911 George V 1¢, 5¢, 10¢, 25¢, 50¢	4500.00
1937 George VI 1¢, 5¢, 10¢, 25¢, 50¢, $1.00	550.00
1937 Similar set, but in card case	450.00

PROOF-LIKE MINT SETS AND SILVER DOLLARS

These are specially minted and handled coins sold by the Royal Canadian Mint for collectors.

Date	Quantity Issued	Sets (6 Coins)	Quantity Issued	Silver Dollars
1954	(Est.) 7,426	200.00	(Est.) 1,268	115.00
1954 Strapless Cent	Incl. above	350.00		
1955	(Est.) 6,301	200.00	(Est.) 5,501	115.00
1955 Arnprior	Incl. above	385.00	Incl. above	300.00
1956	(Est.) 9,018	90.00	(Est.) 6,154	55.00
1957	(Est.) 11,862	75.00	(Est.) 4,379	45.00
1958 Totem Pole	18,259	85.00	14,978	40.00
1959	31,577	40.00	13,583	25.00
1960	64,097	26.00	18,631	16.00
1961	98,373	26.00	22,555	16.00
1962	200,950	17.00	47,591	12.00
1963	673,006	11.00	290,529	9.00
1964	1,653,162	5.75	1,209,279	3.25
1965		5.50		4.50

The majority of mint sets and silver dollars dated before 1954 are not in proof-like condition even though issued by the Royal Canadian Mint.

COINS OF NEWFOUNDLAND — Large Cents
Victoria 1837-1901

Round O
Even
Date

Round O
Low O

G. — *Hair over ear worn through.*
V.G. — *Little detail to the hair over the ear or the braid.*
Fine — *Strands of hair over the ear begin to merge together and the braid is worn.*
V.F. — *The hair over the ear is worn, the braid is clear but no longer sharp.*

Oval O

E.F. — *Slight wear on the hair over the ear and the braid that holds the knot in place is sharp and clear.*

Victoria — Large Cents

Date and Mint Mark	Quantity Minted	G.	V.G.	Fine	V.F.	E.F.	Unc.	B.U.
1865	240,000	1.35	2.00	4.00	8.00	12.00	45.00	95.00
1872H	200,000	1.35	2.00	4.00	8.00	12.00	45.00	95.00
1873	200,025	1.50	2.50	4.50	9.00	13.00	50.00	100.00
1876H	200,000	1.35	2.00	4.00	8.00	12.00	45.00	95.00
1880 Round O, even date . .	400,000	1.35	2.00	4.00	8.00	12.00	40.00	95.00
1880 Round O, low O . . Incl. above		2.00	3.00	5.50	10.00	14.00	50.00	110.00
1880 Oval O, Included in above		60.00	85.00	110.00	150.00	175.00	250.00	425.00
1885	40,000	17.00	25.00	30.00	40.00	50.00	100.00	200.00
1888	50,000	14.00	20.00	25.00	35.00	45.00	90.00	175.00
1890	200,000	1.00	1.75	3.50	6.00	10.00	30.00	60.00
1894	200,000	1.00	1.75	3.50	6.00	10.00	30.00	60.00
1896	200,000	1.00	1.75	3.50	6.00	10.00	30.00	60.00

Edward VII 1901-1910

G. — *Band of crown worn through.*
V.G. — *Band of the crown is worn through at the highest point.*
Fine — *Jewels in the band of crown will be blurred.*
V.F. — *Band of the crown is still clear but no longer sharp.*
E.F. — *Band of the crown slightly worn but generally sharp and clear.*

1904H	100,000	4.50	7.00	11.00	16.00	23.00	45.00	100.00
1907	200,000	1.35	2.00	3.50	6.00	10.00	25.00	50.00
1909	200,000	1.35	2.00	3.50	6.00	10.00	25.00	50.00

COINS OF NEWFOUNDLAND — Large Cents
George V 1910-1936

G. — *Band of crown worn through.*
V.G. — *Band of the crown is worn through at the highest point.*
Fine — *Jewels in the band of crown will be blurred*
V.F. — *Band of the crown is still clear but no longer sharp.*
E.F. — *Band of the crown slightly worn but generally sharp and clear.*

Date and Mint Mark	Quantity Minted	G.	V.G.	Fine	V.F.	E.F.	Unc.	B.U.
1913	400,000	.50	.75	1.50	3.00	5.00	17.00	35.00
1917C	702,350	.40	.60	1.25	3.00	5.00	17.00	35.00
1919C	300,000	.50	.75	1.50	3.00	5.00	17.00	35.00
1920C	302,184	.50	.75	1.50	3.00	5.00	17.00	35.00
1929	300,000	.40	.60	1.25	3.00	5.00	17.00	35.00
1936	300,000	.40	.60	1.25	2.50	4.50	15.00	30.00

SMALL CENTS
George VI 1936-1952

V.G. — *The band is almost worn through. Little detail of the hair.*
Fine — *The band of the crown is considerably worn and the strands of hair begin to merge together.*
V.F. — *Wear extends along the band of the crown and the hair is clear but no longer sharp.*
E.F. — *Band of the crown shows slight wear and the hair is sharp and clear.*

1938	500,000	1.50	2.00	2.50	3.50	9.00	18.00
1940	300,000	5.00	6.00	7.00	9.00	20.00	60.00
1940 Re-engraved Date.		11.00	13.00	15.00	20.00	30.00	90.00
1941C	827,662	.50	.60	.75	1.00	6.00	12.00
1942	1,996,889	.50	.60	.75	1.00	6.00	12.00
1943C	1,239,732	.50	.60	.75	1.00	6.00	12.00
1944C	1,328,776	3.00	3.50	4.00	5.00	17.00	30.00
1947C	313,772	1.50	1.75	2.00	3.00	9.00	18.00

5 CENTS SILVER Victoria 1837-1901

G. — *Braid near ear worn through.*
V.G. — *No details in braid around the ear.*
Fine — *Segments of braid begin to merge into one another.*
V.F. — *Braid is clear but not sharp.*
E.F. — *Braid is slightly worn but generally sharp and clear.*

Date and Mint Mark	Quantity Minted	G.	V.G.	Fine	V.F.	E.F.	Unc.
1865	80,000	15.00	25.00	30.00	40.00	60.00	130.00
1870	40,000	20.00	30.00	35.00	45.00	65.00	150.00
1872H	40,000	15.00	25.00	35.00	40.00	60.00	140.00
1873	44,260	20.00	30.00	35.00	45.00	65.00	150.00
1873H	Included in above	200.00	275.00	375.00	475.00	600.00	1,000
1876H	20,000	25.00	40.00	50.00	75.00	110.00	260.00
1880	40,000	20.00	30.00	45.00	60.00	85.00	200.00
1881	40,000	12.00	18.00	25.00	35.00	60.00	100.00

COINS OF NEWFOUNDLAND — 5 Cents

Date and Mint Mark	Quantity Minted	G.	V.G.	Fine	V.F.	E.F.	Unc.
1882H	60,000	10.00	15.00	20.00	30.00	40.00	100.00
1885	16,000	60.00	85.00	125.00	175.00	250.00	550.00
1888	40,000	10.00	15.00	20.00	30.00	40.00	100.00
1890	160,000	3.50	5.00	9.00	15.00	30.00	75.00
1894	160,000	3.50	5.00	9.00	15.00	30.00	75.00
1896	400,000	2.75	4.00	7.00	15.00	30.00	75.00

Edward VII 1901-1910

G. — Band of crown worn through.
V.G. — Band of the crown is worn through at the highest point.
Fine — Jewels in the band of crown will be blurred.
V.F.— Band of crown still clear but no longer sharp.
E.F. — Band of the crown slightly worn but generally sharp and clear.

		G.	V.G.	Fine	V.F.	E.F.	Unc.
1903	100,000	2.00	3.00	6.00	10.00	23.00	75.00
1904H	100,000	2.00	3.00	6.00	10.00	23.00	75.00
1908	400,000	1.35	2.00	4.00	6.00	15.00	50.00

George V 1910-1936

G. — Band of crown worn through.
V.G. — Band of the crown is worn through at the highest point.
Fine — Jewels in the band of crown will be blurred.
V.F.— Band of crown still clear but no longer sharp.
E.F. — Band of the crown slightly worn but generally sharp and clear.

		G.	V.G.	Fine	V.F.	E.F.	Unc.
1912	300,000	1.00	1.75	3.50	5.50	11.00	35.00
1917C	300,319	1.00	1.75	3.50	5.50	11.00	35.00
1919C	100,844	2.50	3.50	5.50	8.00	15.00	50.00
1929	300,000	.75	1.25	2.50	3.50	7.00	33.00

George VI 1936-1952

V.G. — The band is almost worn through. Little detail of the hair.
Fine — The band of the crown is considerably worn and the strands of hair begin to merge together.
V.F. — Wear extends along the band of the crown and the hair is clear but no longer sharp.
E.F. — Band of the crown shows slight wear and the hair is sharp and clear.

1938	100,000		1.00	1.50	3.00	4.00	15.00
1940C	200,000		.60	.80	1.25	2.50	8.00
1941C	612,641		.35	.55	.85	1.35	7.00
1942C	298,348		1.50	2.00	2.50	3.00	12.00
1943C	351,666		.35	.55	.85	1.35	7.00
1944C	286,504		.80	1.00	1.50	2.50	9.00
1945C	203,828		.35	.50	.75	1.00	6.00
1946C	2,041		150.00	175.00	200.00	250.00	300.00
1947C	38,400		6.00	9.00	12.00	15.00	25.00

COINS OF NEWFOUNDLAND — 10 Cents

10 Cents — Victoria 1837-1901

G. — Braid around ear worn through.
V.G. — No details in braid around the ear.
Fine — Segments of braid begin to merge into one another.
V.F. — Braid is clear but not sharp.
E.F. — Braid is slightly worn but generally sharp and clear.

Date and Mint Mark	Quantity Minted	G.	V.G.	Fine	V.F.	E.F.	Unc.
1865	80,000	10.00	15.00	20.00	25.00	50.00	125.00
1870	30,000	85.00	125.00	200.00	250.00	350.00	600.00
1872H	40,000	5.00	8.00	15.00	20.00	40.00	115.00
1873	23,614	9.00	13.00	20.00	25.00	45.00	125.00
1876H	10,000	17.00	25.00	35.00	50.00	100.00	250.00
1880	10,000	17.00	25.00	35.00	50.00	100.00	250.00
1882H	20,000	7.50	10.00	15.00	25.00	45.00	110.00
1885	8,000	25.00	40.00	60.00	80.00	160.00	300.00
1888	30,000	7.00	10.00	15.00	25.00	45.00	110.00
1890	100,000	2.25	3.25	7.00	15.00	30.00	80.00
1894	100,000	2.25	3.25	7.00	15.00	30.00	80.00
1896	230,000	2.00	2.75	6.00	12.00	25.00	75.00

Edward VII 1901-1910

G. — Band of crown worn through.
V.G. — Band of the crown is worn through at the highest point.
Fine — Jewels in band of crown will be blurred.
V.F. — Band of the crown is still clear but no longer sharp.
E.F. — Band of the crown slightly worn but generally sharp and clear.

1903	100,000	2.00	3.00	6.00	12.00	25.00	80.00
1904H	100,000	2.00	3.00	6.00	12.00	25.00	80.00

George V 1910-1936

G. — Band of crown worn through.
V.G. — Band of the crown is worn through at the highest point.
Fine — Jewels in band of crown will be blurred.
V.F. — Band of the crown is still clear but no longer sharp.
E.F. — Band of the crown slightly worn but generally sharp and clear.

1912	150,000	1.50	2.25	4.50	9.00	20.00	70.00
1917C	250,805	1.00	1.50	3.25	7.00	15.00	70.00
1919C	54,342	3.00	5.00	10.00	15.00	25.00	75.00

George VI 1936-1952

V.G. — The band is almost worn through. Little detail of the hair.
Fine — Band of crown is considerably worn and the strands of hair begin to merge together.
V.F. — Wear extends along band of crown and the hair is clear but no longer sharp.
E.F. — Band of the crown shows slight wear and the hair is sharp and clear.

1938	100,000			.75	1.25	2.50	4.50	15.00

Date and Mint Mark	Quantity Minted	G.	V.G.	Fine	V.F.	E.F.	Unc.
1940................100,000			.75	1.25	2.50	4.50	12.00
1941C..............483,630			.45	.70	1.25	3.50	11.00
1942C..............292,736			.45	.70	1.25	3.50	11.00
1943C..............104,706			.45	.70	1.25	3.50	11.00
1944C..............151,471			.75	1.00	2.00	4.00	12.00
1945C..............175,833			.40	.60	1.00	3.00	10.00
1946C...............38,400		6.00	8.00	10.00	12.00		35.00
1947C...............61,988		3.00	4.00	5.00	7.00		20.00

20 CENTS
Victoria 1837-1901

G. — Braid around ear worn through.
V.G. — No details in braid around the ear.
Fine — Segments of braid begin to merge into one another.
V.F. — Braid is clear but not sharp.
E.F. — Braid is slightly worn but generally sharp and clear.

		G.	V.G.	Fine	V.F.	E.F.	Unc.
1865................100,000		4.50	7.00	12.00	20.00	40.00	125.00
1870.................50,000		8.00	12.00	20.00	30.00	55.00	175.00
1872H................90,000		4.50	7.00	12.00	18.00	35.00	125.00
1873................45,797		4.50	7.00	14.00	20.00	40.00	135.00
1876H................50,000		7.00	10.00	18.00	30.00	60.00	165.00
1880.................30,000		7.00	10.00	18.00	30.00	60.00	175.00
1881................60,000		2.00	3.00	4.00	8.00	25.00	100.00
1882H...............100,000		1.75	2.50	3.50	7.00	25.00	80.00
1885................40,000		2.50	3.50	5.00	10.00	25.00	90.00
1888................75,000		2.00	3.00	4.50	9.00	25.00	80.00
1890................100,000		1.00	1.50	2.50	7.00	20.00	70.00
1894................100,000		1.00	1.50	2.50	7.00	20.00	70.00

Narrow Date   Wide Date

		G.	V.G.	Fine	V.F.	E.F.	Unc.
1896 Narrow Date......125,000		1.00	1.50	2.50	6.00	20.00	60.00
1896 Wide Date.....Incl. above		1.50	2.50	3.50	7.00	25.00	80.00
1899 Wide Date........125,000		.75	1.25	2.50	5.00	10.00	55.00
1899 Narrow Date..Incl. above		2.00	3.00	4.50	7.00	15.00	75.00
1900................125,000		.75	1.25	2.25	4.50	9.00	55.00

Edward VII 1901-1910

G. — Band of crown worn through.
V.G. — Band of the crown is worn through at the highest point.
Fine — Jewels in the band of crown will be blurred.
V.F. — Band of the crown is still clear but no longer sharp.
E.F. — Band of the crown slightly worn but generally sharp and clear.

1904H................75,000		4.00	6.00	8.00	10.00	30.00	100.00

COINS OF NEWFOUNDLAND — 20, 25 and 50 Cents

20 and 25 Cents — George V 1910-1936

G. — *Band of crown worn through.*
V.G. — *Band of the crown is worn through at the highest point.*
Fine — *Jewels in the band of crown will be blurred.*
V.F. — *Band of the crown is still clear but no longer sharp.*
E.F. — *Band of the crown slightly worn but generally sharp and clear.*

Date and Mint Mark	Quantity Minted	G.	V.G.	Fine	V.F.	E.F.	Unc.
1912 20 Cents	350,000	.75	1.00	1.50	4.00	12.00	40.00
1917C 25 Cents	464,779	.50	.75	1.25	2.25	4.50	20.00
1919C 25 Cents	163,939	.85	1.25	2.00	3.00	5.50	25.00

50 CENTS — Victoria 1837-1901

G. — *Braid around ear worn through.*

V.G. — *No details in braid around the ear.*

Fine — *Segments of braid begin to merge into one another.*

V.F. — *Braid is clear but not sharp.*

E.F. — *Braid is slightly worn but generally sharp and clear.*

Date	Quantity	G.	V.G.	Fine	V.F.	E.F.	Unc.
1870	50,000	5.00	8.00	12.00	20.00	50.00	235.00
1872H	48,000	5.00	8.00	12.00	20.00	50.00	235.00
1873	37,675	5.00	8.00	12.00	20.00	50.00	235.00
1874	80,000	5.00	8.00	12.00	20.00	50.00	235.00
1876H	28,000	8.00	12.00	20.00	30.00	75.00	335.00
1880	24,000	8.00	12.00	20.00	30.00	75.00	335.00
1881	50,000	4.50	7.00	12.00	20.00	55.00	235.00
1882H	100,000	3.50	5.00	8.00	14.00	40.00	235.00
1885	40,000	4.50	7.00	12.00	18.00	45.00	235.00
1888	20,000	7.50	10.00	15.00	25.00	75.00	275.00
1894	40,000	2.75	4.00	6.00	12.00	35.00	185.00
1896	60,000	2.00	3.00	5.00	11.00	35.00	185.00
1898	79,607	1.35	2.00	4.00	10.00	28.00	185.00

Narrow "9's"   Wide "9's"

Date	Quantity	G.	V.G.	Fine	V.F.	E.F.	Unc.
1899 Narrow 9's	150,000	1.35	2.00	4.00	10.00	28.00	185.00
1899 Wide 9's	Incl. above	1.35	2.00	4.00	10.00	28.00	185.00
1900	150,000	1.00	1.50	3.00	9.00	25.00	175.00

COINS OF NEWFOUNDLAND — 50 Cents
Edward VII 1901-1910

G. — *Band of crown is worn through.*

V.G. — *Band of the crown is worn through at the highest point.*

Fine — *Jewels in the band of crown will be blurred.*

V.F. — *Band of the crown is still clear but no longer sharp.*

E.F. — *Band of the crown slightly worn but generally sharp and clear.*

Date and Mint Mark	Quantity Minted	G.	V.G.	Fine	V.F.	E.F.	Unc.
1904H	140,000	1.00	1.50	3.00	9.00	18.00	100.00
1907	100,000	1.25	1.75	3.50	10.00	20.00	110.00
1908	160,000	.85	1.35	2.75	8.00	16.00	95.00
1909	200,000	.75	1.25	2.50	7.50	15.00	90.00

George V 1910-1936

G. — *Band of crown is worn through.*

V.G. — *Band of the crown is worn through at the highest point.*

Fine — *Jewels in the band of crown will be blurred.*

V.F. — *Band of the crown is still clear but no longer sharp.*

E.F. — *Band of the crown slightly worn but generally sharp and clear.*

1911	200,000	.85	1.25	2.50	7.50	18.00	70.00
1917C	375,560	.75	1.00	2.50	7.00	15.00	60.00
1918C	294,824	.75	1.00	2.50	7.00	15.00	55.00
1919C	306,267	.75	1.00	2.50	7.00	15.00	55.00

2 DOLLARS GOLD—Victoria 1837-1901

Fine — *Segments of braid begin to merge into one another.*

V.F. — *Braid is clear but not sharp.*

E.F. — *Braid is slightly worn but generally sharp and clear.*

1865	10,000	45.00	60.00	70.00	90.00
1870	10,000	45.00	60.00	70.00	90.00
1872	6,050	90.00	110.00	130.00	175.00
1880	2,500	275.00	350.00	450.00	550.00
1881	10,000	45.00	50.00	60.00	75.00
1882H	25,000	35.00	40.00	45.00	60.00
1885	10,000	45.00	50.00	55.00	75.00
1888	25,000	35.00	40.00	45.00	60.00

CANADA AND NEWFOUNDLAND PAPER MONEY

Introduction

The tremendous growth of interest in Canadian coins and tokens in recent years has now extended to the field of paper money. A complete listing of the Government and Bank of Canada notes is badly needed and it is felt that this section will fill a long-felt want.

Canada's note issues now go back for nearly a century. In that time they have illustrated many individuals who have a place in the country's history, while the vignettes in many cases deal with various aspects of the country's agricultural and industrial life.

It is of interest to note that, since 1870, only the Dominion Government, first through the Department of Finance, and since 1935 through the Bank of Canada, has issued one- and two-dollar bills. The reason for this may not be generally known. Bills of these denominations were, and to a considerable extent still are, those most generally found in circulation. In former days, when the value of money was much greater, such bills were likely to be almost the only ones ever handled by the poorer or less literate members of the community. As readers of C. S. Howard's admirable paper "Canadian Banks and Bank-notes" will recall, a large number of private banks had issued one- and two-dollar bills in the early days, and had subsequently failed, while the unwary had also to contend with the bills of "phantom" banks, which were a pure swindle. In these circumstances, it was felt that notes of these denominations should be issued by the Dominion Government, so that they might be accepted with confidence by all and sundry as being "as good as gold," which, for the greater part of their history, they were.

The values quoted are based on rarity and recent auction and retail prices: they are neither buying nor selling offers, but give a fair indication of market values at the time of publication.

Illustrations of notes are in a reduced size.

The asterisk in front of a catalogue number indicates that the note is illustrated.

TITLE ABBREVIATIONS

H.M. . . . . . . His Majesty or Her Majesty.
T.R.H . . . . . Their Royal Highnesses.
H.R.H . . . . . His, or Her, Royal Highness.
K.G . . . . Knight of the Garter.
K.T . . . . Knight of the Thistle.
K.P . . . . Knight of St. Patrick.
G.M.B. ⎫ These indicate various degrees of the Order of the Bath—Grand
G.C.B. ⎪ Master, Knight Grand Cross, Knight Commander, and Com-
K.C.B. ⎬ panion. The Order is one of the oldest in existence, having been
C.B. ⎭ instituted in 1399.

O.M.......Order of Merit.
G.C.S.I....Knight Grand Commander of the Star of India.
G.C.M.G...Knight Grand Cross of the Order of St. Michael and St. George.
G.C.I.E....Knight Grand Commander of the Order of the Indian Empire.
G.C.V.O...Knight Grand Cross of the Royal Victorian Order.
G.B.E.....Knight Grand Cross of the Order of the British Empire.
V.D.......Volunteer Officer's Decoration.
T.D.......Territorial Decoration.

REGNAL DATES

Victoria	1837-1901	Edward VIII	1936
Edward VII	1901-1910	George VI	1936-1952
George V	1910-1936	Elizabeth II	1952-

DEFINITION OF PAPER MONEY CONDITIONS

Unc.—Uncirculated. Crisp new condition, without pin holes or creases.

E.F.—Extremely Fine. In new condition but with minor pin holes or creases.

V.F.—Very Fine. Shows only slight signs of being in circulation.

F.—Fine. Has been in circulation for some time, but is still firm and without noticeable fading.

V.G.—Very Good. A whole note with slight signs of edge fraying and some fading of colours.

Countersigned signatures in ink are not listed, since in practically every instance they are the signatures of junior employees of the Department and varied from day to day. Many of these signatures are impossible to decipher, and the Government kept no record of them.

—➤ *CAUTION—Collectors of paper money should be on guard against counterfeit notes. Your banker might point out to you several methods which may be used to detect spurious notes.*

Moisten fingers and rub against the serial number. The ink on bogus notes often smears.

Examine the portrait. Counterfeit notes do not always have the high-grade engraving of genuine notes.

Feel the paper. A good quality rag and cotton paper is used for genuine notes, while counterfeit notes are often printed on a lower-grade smooth paper.

First brought into use as a result of scarcity of regular currency — and as a temporary expedient—Playing Card Money nevertheless remained in common use for a period of approximately 75 years in French Canada. Full cards, half cards, quarter cards and even portions of clipped cards were used. Genuine specimens are extremely rare.

Card Money Illustrations are Full Size.

PLAYING CARD MONEY

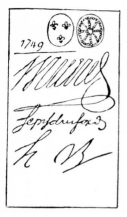

CANADA'S FIRST BANK NOTE
Issued in 1792

(Illustration ½ Size)

DOMINION OF CANADA NOTES

25 Cent Fractional Currency (Shinplasters)

Webster defines "shinplaster," in the numismatic sense, as:

"A piece of unsecured or poorly secured paper money, especially one greatly depreciated in value."

"A piece of government paper money of a denomination less than a dollar."

"Any of the notes of small value issued by private bankers during the depression of 1837."

Unquestionably, the second of these definitions is the only one that covers the fractional notes of Canada. They are, and always have been, redeemable at full face value.

The first issue, that of 1870, appears to have been in the nature of an emergency issue. Both the banks and the government had become seriously worried by the amount of United States silver coinage at that time circulating in Canada, in default of any adequate supply of regnal coins. Their worry arose from the fact that the U.S. dollar was at the time worth just eighty cents in Canada, with the result that those trusting individuals who had accepted U.S. silver at face found, when they came to bank it, that they were faced with a twenty per cent loss. The government, therefore, decided to take steps to call in the U.S. silver and to replace it by an issue of Canadian coins. As some time was bound to elapse before these coins would be available, and as it was desired to withdraw the U.S. coins without further delay, it was decided to meet the inevitable shortage of small change that was bound to ensue by issuing the twenty-five cent notes. It seems clear that the issue was never intended to be more than temporary in nature, but evidently the small notes were found useful in many ways and, so far from their being systematically withdrawn, the government was compelled to make further issues in 1900 and 1923.

More than 5 million of these notes were in circulation in 1929, but since then the number has steadily declined. In 1935 the Bank of Canada decided to recall all "shinplasters" from circulation, and as a result, these interesting souvenirs of bygone days are now seldom seen. Some are in the hands of numismatists, others are treasured family keepsakes.

The 25¢ notes were frequently given to children as souvenirs. They were used to a great extent by godparents, especially in the Province of Quebec, as gifts to their godchildren.

In the days when facilities for sending small amounts by mail were not as efficient as they are today, they were frequently enclosed in letters.

Many attribute the expression "shinplaster" to the use of such bills by soldiers of the Revolutionary War period as a lining to prevent their shoes from chafing.

DOMINION OF CANADA NOTES (Shinplasters)

No.	Date	Portrait, Design, Etc. Signatures	V.G.	Fine	V.F.	E.F.	Unc.
*1	March 1, 1870	Britannia.........W. Dickinson—T. D. Harington	4.00	8.00	15.00	25.00	45.00
*1a	March 1, 1870	Britannia, Letter "A" under 1870 at left.......W. Dickinson—T. D. Harington	40.00	60.00	80.00	100.00	185.00
1b	March 1, 1870	Britannia, Letter "B" under 1870 at left.........W. Dickinson—T. D. Harington					
*2	Jan. 2, 1900	Britannia seated.............J. M. Courtney	6.00	12.00	25.00	35.00	65.00
*3	Jan. 2, 1900	Britannia seated.............T. C. Boville	3.00	4.00	8.00	11.00	25.00
*4	Jan. 2, 1900	Britannia seated.............J. C. Saunders	2.00	3.00	5.00	8.00	18.00
*5	July 2, 1923	Britannia, has "Authorized by R.S.C. Cap. 31" at left.........G. W. Hyndman—J. C. Saunders	5.00	8.00	15.00	20.00	40.00
			13.00	17.00	25.00	30.00	55.00

(A red letter prefixes the number on No. 5 notes. Any one of the following — A, B, C, D, E, H, J, K, L, M.)

6

7

8

No.	Date	Portrait, Design, Etc.	Signatures	V. G.	Fine	V. F.	E. F.	Unc.
*6	July 2, 1923	Brit., without Auth., etc.	G. W. Hyndman — J. C. Saunders	11.00	15.00	20.00	25.00	45.00
*7	July 2, 1923	Britannia	S. P. McCavour — J. C. Saunders	2.00	2.50	4.00	6.00	15.00
*8	July 2, 1923	Britannia	C. E. Campbell — W. C. Clark	2.25	3.00	5.00	7.00	18.00

ONE DOLLAR NOTES

$1   1870—The portrait of Jacques Cartier is taken from a painting by F. Riss (circa 1804-1866) which hangs in the Hôtel de Ville of St. Malo, the port from which Cartier sailed on his memorable voyage to the New World in 1534, as a result of which France took possession of what is now Canada. Riss is said to have taken as his model a pen drawing in the Bibliothèque Nationale, Paris, but this drawing has never been located.

9

*9	July 1, 1870	Jacques Cartier (Rev. Montreal)	W. Dickinson — T. D. Harington	65.00	75.00	100.00	125.00	185.00
9a	As No. 9 but "Payable at Toronto" on rev.	W. Dickinson — T. D. Harington	60.00	70.00	90.00	115.00	175.00
9b	As No. 9 but "Payable at Halifax" on rev.	W. Dickinson — T. D. Harington	100.00	150.00	200.00	250.00	350.00
9c	As No. 9 but "Payable at St. John" on rev.	W. Dickinson — T. D. Harington	100.00	150.00	200.00	250.00	350.00

11

$1 1878—The Countess of Dufferin, wife of the Earl of Dufferin, K.P., K.C.B., G.C.M.G., Governor General of Canada 1872-78.

14

10

12

$1 1897-8.—The Earl and Countess of Aberdeen. The Earl of Aberdeen, K.T., G.C.M.G., was Governor General 1893-98. Few occupants of Rideau Hall have entered more wholeheartedly into the life of Canada than the Aberdeens. Lady Aberdeen was a moving spirit in the formation of two bodies that continue to this day as major factors in Canadian life—the National Council of Women and the Victorian Order of Nurses, of both of which she was the first President.

It is only in comparatively recent times that Canada has become a great exporting nation, in the industrial sense. Even in the agricultural sense, it was only after the settlement of the prairies that agricultural products began to take a major place in her economy. For the greater part of her history, her forests and her fur-bearers provided her major exports, and both have maintained their importance to the present.

In the early days of the logging industry, the waterways were practically the only means of transporting the logs, and even today the bulk of the cut travels to the mill chiefly by water. One result of this was that settlements that depended on the industry either directly or indirectly sprang up along the river banks all over Eastern Canada, and most of them persist to this day, even though they may no longer depend on the forest for their existence.

16

15

$1   1911—The Earl and Countess of Grey. Earl Grey, G.C.M.G., was Governor General 1904-11.

No.	Date	Portrait, Design, Etc.	Signatures	V.G.	Fine	V.F.	E.F.	Unc.
*10	June 1, 1878	Countess of Dufferin (Rev. Montreal)......	T. D. Harington	35.00	45.00	55.00	75.00	125.00
10a		Same as No. 10 but has "Payable at Toronto" on reverse..	T. D. Harington	35.00	45.00	55.00	75.00	125.00
10b		Same as No. 10 but has "Payable at Halifax" on reverse..	T. D. Harington	90.00	140.00	175.00	200.00	275.00
10c		Same as No. 10 but has "Payable at St. John" on rev.....	T. D. Harington	100.00	150.00	200.00	250.00	300.00
(Notes 10 to 10c have a plain obverse border, notes 11 to 11c a lettered border.)								
*11	June 1, 1878	Countess of Dufferin (Rev. Montreal).......	T. D. Harington	25.00	35.00	45.00	60.00	110.00
11a		Same as No. 11 but has "Payable at Toronto" on reverse..	T. D. Harington	25.00	35.00	45.00	60.00	110.00
11b		Same as No. 11 but has "Payable at Halifax" on reverse..	T. D. Harington	80.00	125.00	150.00	175.00	225.00
11c		Same as No. 11 but has "Payable at St. John" on rev.....	T. D. Harington	90.00	140.00	175.00	200.00	275.00
*12	July 2, 1897	Earl & Countess of Aberdeen & Logging Scene.	J. M. Courtney	35.00	45.00	55.00	75.00	125.00
13	Mar. 31, 1898	Earl & Countess of Aberdeen & Logging Scene.	J. M. Courtney	10.00	15.00	20.00	25.00	50.00
*14	Mar. 31, 1898	Earl & Countess of Aberdeen & Logging Scene.	T. C. Boville	12.00	17.00	23.00	30.00	55.00
*15	Jan. 3, 1911	Earl & Countess of Grey (Green line over signatures)	T. C. Boville	8.00	10.00	14.00	18.00	40.00
*16	Jan. 3, 1911	Same as No. 15 but has black line over signatures...........		7.00	9.00	13.00	17.00	35.00

17A

17

19

20

$1 1917—H.R.H. Princess Patricia of Connaught (now Lady Patricia Ramsay), daughter of T.R.H. the Duke and Duchess of Connaught. On the outbreak of war in 1914, A. Hamilton Gault, of Montreal, offered the government $100,000 for the purpose of raising a regiment of light infantry. Princess Patricia permitted the regiment to be designated "Princess Patricia's Canadian Light Infantry," herself worked the first regimental colours, and became Colonel-in-Chief. Previous active service was essential for would-be recruits, and the regiment built up, and has since been maintained, a record second to none in the armed forces of Canada.

No.	Date	Portrait, Design, Etc.	Signatures	V.G.	Fine	V.F.	E.F.	Unc.
*17	Mar. 17, 1917	Same as No. 17a but without Am. Bk. Note Co.	T. C. Boville	7.00	9.00	13.00	17.00	35.00
*17a	Mar. 17, 1917	Princess Pat. with Am. Bk. Note Co. on obv., rev.	T. C. Boville	7.00	9.00	13.00	17.00	35.00
18	March 17, 1917	Same as No. 17a but with signature.........	J. C. Saunders	7.50	10.00	14.00	18.00	38.00
*19	Mar. 17, 1917	Same (Bl. seal over "one")	G. W. Hyndman — J. C. Saunders	8.00	11.00	15.00	20.00	40.00
*20	Mar. 17, 1917	Princess Pat. (Black seal)	G. W. Hyndman — J. C. Saunders	8.00	11.00	15.00	20.00	40.00

$1 1923—His Majesty King George V. 1910-1936.

24

25

$2 1870—Generals Wolfe and Montcalm, leaders of the British and French forces in the Battle of the Plains of Abraham, 1759, by which Britain wrested Canada from France, and in which both generals lost their lives.

No.	Date	Portrait, Design, Etc.	Signatures	V. G.	Fine	V. F.	E. F.	Unc.
21	July 2, 1923	King Geo. V (Black seal)	G. W. Hyndman — J. C. Saunders	10.00	12.00	15.00	20.00	35.00
22	July 2, 1923	King Geo. V (Black seal)	S. P. McCavour — J. C. Saunders	6.00	8.00	12.00	17.00	30.00
22a	July 2, 1923	King Geo. V (Blue seal)	S. P. McCavour — J. C. Saunders	6.00	8.00	12.00	15.00	27.00
22b	July 2, 1923	King Geo. V (Green seal)	S. P. McCavour — J. C. Saunders	5.00	7.00	10.00	13.00	25.00
22c	July 2, 1923	King Geo. V (Red seal)	S. P. McCavour — J. C. Saunders	5.00	7.00	10.00	13.00	25.00
22d	July 2, 1923	King George V (Purple-Brown seal)	S. P. McCavour — J. C. Saunders	5.00	7.00	10.00	13.00	25.00
22e	July 2, 1923	King Geo. V (Lilac seal)	S. P. McCavour — J. C. Saunders	35.00	45.00	55.00	65.00	100.00
23	July 2, 1923	King George V (Black seal)	C. E. Campbell — W. Sellar	4.00	5.00	7.50	10.00	20.00
23a	July 2, 1923	King George V (Lilac seal)	C. E. Campbell — W. Sellar	75.00	100.00	125.00	150.00	200.00
*24	July 2, 1923	King Geo. V (Black seal)	C. E. Campbell — W. C. Clark	4.00	5.00	7.00	9.00	18.00

TWO DOLLAR NOTES

No.	Date	Portrait, Design, Etc.	Signatures	V. G.	Fine	V. F.	E. F.	Unc.
*25	July 1, 1870	Wolfe and Montcalm (Rev. Montreal)	W. Dickinson — T. D. Harington	100.00	150.00	200.00	250.00	350.00
25a		As No. 25 but "Payable at Toronto" on rev.	W. Dickinson—T. D. Harington	100.00	150.00	200.00	250.00	350.00
25b		As No. 25 but "Payable at Halifax" on rev.	W. Dickinson—T. D. Harington	150.00	200.00	275.00	350.00	500.00
25c		Same as No. 25 but has "Payable at St. John" on reverse	W. Dickinson — T. D. Harington	150.00	200.00	275.00	350.00	500.00

26

$2 1878—Earl of Dufferin, K.P., K.C.B., G.C.M.G., Governor General of Canada 1872-78.

27

$2 1887—The Marquis and Marchioness of Lansdowne. The Marquis of Lansdowne was Governor General 1883-88.

$2 1897—H.R.H. Edward, Prince of Wales, eldest son of Queen Victoria, on whose death he ascended the throne as Edward VII. The cod fisheries of the Grand Banks of Newfoundland have drawn fishermen from Europe for many centuries past, and still do. The vignette on the two dollar bill of 1897 shows a typical dory with its oil-skinned crew busy gaffing the cod that have been taken in the net. As those who have read Kipling's "Captains Courageous" know, the Banks form a cosmopolitan city on the waters, where fishermen from the Maritimes, from New England, and from Europe gather annually to reap the harvest of the sea.

28

No.	Date	Portrait, Design, Etc.	Signatures	V.G.	Fine	V.F.	E.F.	Unc.
*26	June 1, 1878	Earl of Dufferin (Rev. Montreal)	T. D. Harington	60.00	70.00	80.00	100.00	150.00
26a		Same as No. 26 but has "Payable at Toronto" on reverse	T. D. Harington	75.00	85.00	100.00	125.00	200.00
26b		Same as No. 26 but has "Payable at Halifax" on reverse	T. D. Harington	150.00	200.00	275.00	350.00	500.00
26c		Same as No. 26 but has "Payable at St. John" on reverse	T. D. Harington	150.00	200.00	275.00	350.00	500.00
*27	July 2, 1887	Marquis and Marchioness of Lansdowne	J. M. Courtney	40.00	50.00	60.00	75.00	100.00
*28	July 2, 1897	Prince of Wales — Fishing Scene	J. M. Courtney	15.00	25.00	30.00	40.00	60.00
29	July 2, 1897	Prince of Wales — Fishing Scene	T. C. Boville	17.00	27.00	35.00	45.00	70.00

DOMINION OF CANADA NOTES

32

30

34

$2 1914—T.R.H. the Duke and Duchess of Connaught. Field Marshal H.R.H. the Duke of Connaught, K.G., P.C., K.T., G.M.B., G.C.S.I., G.C.M.G., G.C.I.E., G.C.V.O., G.B.E., V.D., T.D., third son of Queen Victoria, and godson of the great Duke of Wellington, was Governor General 1911-1916.

No.	Date	Portrait, Design, Etc.	Signatures	V. G.	Fine	V. F.	E. F.	Unc.
*30	Jan. 2, 1914	Connaughts (No seal, "Will pay - -" is curved)	T. C. Boville	9.00	14.00	18.00	23.00	30.00
31	Jan. 2, 1914	Connaughts (No seal, "Will pay - -" is straight)	T. C. Boville	10.00	15.00	20.00	25.00	35.00
*32	Jan. 2, 1914	Connaughts (No seal)	J. C. Saunders	15.00	20.00	25.00	30.00	35.00
33	Jan. 2, 1914	Connaughts (Seal over "Two")	G. W. Hyndman — J. C. Saunders	35.00	45.00	60.00	75.00	100.00
*34	Jan. 2, 1914	Connaughts (Black seal)	G. W. Hyndman — J. C. Saunders	10.00	15.00	20.00	30.00	40.00

36

39

$2 1923—H.R.H. Edward, Prince of Wales, eldest son of George V, in the uniform of the Welsh Guards. He succeeded his father as Edward VIII on January 20, 1936, and abdicated in favour of his brother, the Duke of York, on December 10, 1936. The first act of H.M. King George VI was to create his brother a Royal Duke with the title of Windsor.

$4 1882—The Marquis of Lorne, K.T., G.C.M.G., Governor General, 1878-1883. The Marquis married H.R.H. Princess Louise, a daughter of Queen Victoria, and later succeeded his father as Duke of Argyll. The Marquis and his wife, who was herself a distinguished painter and sculptor, were especially interested in fostering the development of the arts in the Dominion, and it was chiefly owing to the Marquis' efforts that the Royal Canadian Academy of Art was founded in 1880, and the Royal Society of Canada in 1881.

No.	Date	Portrait, Design, Etc.	Signatures	V.G.	Fine	V.F.	E.F.	Unc.
35	June 23, 1923	Prince of Wales (Blk. seal)	G. W. Hyndman — J. C. Saunders	10.00	13.00	18.00	25.00	40.00
*36	June 23, 1923	Prince of Wales (Blk. seal)	S. P. McCavour — J. C. Saunders	8.00	10.00	15.00	20.00	30.00
36a	June 23, 1923	Prince of Wales (Blue seal)	S. P. McCavour — J. C. Saunders	8.00	10.00	15.00	20.00	30.00
36b	June 23, 1923	Prince of Wales (Green seal)	S. P. McCavour — J. C. Saunders	8.00	10.00	15.00	20.00	30.00
36c	June 23, 1923	Prince of Wales (Red seal)	S. P. McCavour — J. C. Saunders	8.00	10.00	15.00	20.00	30.00
36d	June 23, 1923	Prince of Wales (Purple-brown seal)	S. P. McCavour — J. C. Saunders	8.00	10.00	15.00	20.00	30.00
37	June 23, 1923	Prince of Wales (Black seal)	C. E. Campbell — W. Sellar	7.00	9.00	13.00	18.00	28.00
37a	June 23, 1923	Prince of Wales (Blue seal)	C. E. Campbell — W. Sellar	9.00	11.00	17.00	22.00	35.00
38	June 23, 1923	Prince of Wales (Blk. seal)	C. E. Campbell — W. C. Clark	7.00	9.00	13.00	18.00	28.00

FOUR DOLLAR NOTES

No.	Date	Portrait, Design, Etc.	Signatures	V.G.	Fine	V.F.	E.F.	Unc.
*39	May 1, 1882	Marquis of Lorne	J. M. Courtney	175.00	200.00	250.00	300.00	400.00

(Colour of seal on No. 39 varies from brown to orange, probably the result of oxidation.)

41

40

$4   1900-2—The Earl and Countess of Minto. The Earl of Minto, G.C.M.G., was Governor General 1898-1904. Both the Earl and Countess were enthusiastic figure-skaters, and it was owing to their efforts that the Minto Skating Club, one of the leading bodies in the skating world, was founded.

These bills showed, as their central feature, the great locks at Sault Ste. Marie. By a curious oversight, the 1900 bill showed the Unites States lock. The error was corrected on the 1902 issue.

42

These locks are some of the largest in the world. The Canadian lock is 900 feet long, 60 feet wide, and 18.25 feet deep. Few people seem aware of the tremendous volume of traffic handled by these locks. In a recent ten-year period they have carried about double the tonnage that carried by the Panama Canal.

No.	Date	Portrait, Design, Etc.	Signatures	V. G.	Fine	V. F.	E. F.	Unc.
*40	July 2, 1900	Earl & Countess of Minto (American Locks)	J. M. Courtney	80.00	110.00	150.00	225.00	325.00
*41	Jan. 2, 1902	Earl & Countess of Minto (Canadian Locks)	J. M. Courtney	100.00	125.00	175.00	250.00	375.00
*42	Jan. 2, 1902	Same as No. 41 but "FOUR" in place of "4" and signature	T. C. Boville	85.00	115.00	155.00	250.00	350.00

44

43

45

$5   1912—It only requires a glance at a map to drive home the realization that the railways are the lifelines of Canada. As a link between east and west they are indispensable, and are likely to remain so. In the movement of bulk commodities such as wheat and coal, and in transporting passengers in numbers over long distances they have no substitutes. The development of the West really began with the completion of the Canadian Pacific Railway to Vancouver in 1885, and progress was so rapid that the Canadian Northern (now part of the Canadian National Railways) pushed through a second line that reached Vancouver in 1915.

FIVE DOLLAR NOTES

No.	Date	Portrait, Design, Etc.	Signatures	V.G.	Fine	V.F.	E.F.	Unc.
*43	May 1, 1912	Train (Without blue seal)	T. C. Boville	17.00	20.00	25.00	30.00	40.00
*44	May 1, 1912	Train (Blue seal over "FIVE")	G. W. Hyndman — T. C. Boville	30.00	35.00	40.00	50.00	80.00
44a	Same, but		G. W. Hyndman — J. C. Saunders	50.00	70.00	90.00	110.00	150.00
*45	May 1, 1912	Train (Blue seal)	G. W. Hyndman — J. C. Saunders	17.00	20.00	25.00	30.00	40.00

$5 1924—H.M. Queen Mary, consort of King George V. Her Majesty, a great-granddaughter of George III, was the daughter of the Duke of Teck, who married H.R.H. Princess Marie Adelaide of Cambridge. Before her death in 1953 she saw two of her sons and her granddaughter, Queen Elizabeth II, succeed to throne. The 1924 $5.00 issue has been found extremely elusive by a generation of collectors, and the suggestion is advanced that most specimens were held as bank reserves and only a few allowed to reach circulation at the time when the new, small-format chartered bank currency was in preparation.

$1000 1925—H.M. Queen Mary.

*46 May 26, 1924 Queen Mary (Black seal) ... C. E. Campbell — Watson Sellar 100.00 150.00 200.00 250.00 300.00

$500 1925—H.M. King George V, 1910-1936.
$1000 1911—H.M. King George V, 1910-1936.

$50 NOTE	47	March 1, 1872 Allegorical Vignette	T. D. Harington	Very Rare
$500 NOTES	48	Jan. 3, 1911 Queen Mary		Very Rare
	*49	Jan. 2, 1925 King George V		Very Rare
$1000 NOTES	50	Jan. 3, 1911 King George V		Very Rare
	*51	Jan. 2, 1925 Queen Mary		Very Rare

Notes for use between the chartered banks and not for general circulation.

47A	$100	Mar. 1, 1872 Parliament Building (V. Rare)	54	$1,000	Jan. 2, 1901 Earl Roberts
47B	$500	July 1, 1871 Queen Victoria (Very Rare)	55	$1,000	Jan. 2, 1924 Earl Roberts
49B	$1,000	July 1, 1871 Allegorical Vignette (V. Rare)	56	$5,000	July 2, 1896 Sir John A. Macdonald
52	$500	July 2, 1896 Marquis of Lorne	57	$5,000	Jan. 2, 1901 Queen Victoria
53	$1,000	July 2, 1896 Queen Victoria			

57A $5,000 Jan. 2, 1918 Queen Victoria
58 $5,000 Jan. 2, 1924 Queen Victoria

59 $50,000 Jan. 2, 1918 King Geo. V & Queen Mary
60 $50,000 Jan. 2, 1924 King Geo. V & Queen Mary

The Province came into being in 1841 by the parliamentary union of Upper and Lower Canada (now known as Ontario and Quebec) and ceased to exist with Confederation in 1867.

PROVINCE OF CANADA NOTES — DATED OCT. 1, 1866

No.	Note	Portrait, Design, Etc.	Signature	V.G.	Fine	V.F.	E.F.	Unc.
*61	$1	Champlain and Cartier, payable at Montreal	T. D. Harington	70.00	85.00	100.00	125.00	175.00
61a	$1	Same, but payable at Toronto	T. D. Harington	70.00	85.00	100.00	125.00	175.00
61b	$1	Same, but payable at Halifax	T. D. Harington	100.00	125.00	150.00	200.00	250.00
*62	$2	Indian Girl—Sailor Boy with lion, payable at Mont.	T. D. Harington	80.00	95.00	110.00	150.00	200.00
62a	$2	Same, but payable at Toronto	T. D. Harington	80.00	95.00	110.00	150.00	200.00
62b	$2	Same, but payable at Halifax	T. D. Harington	110.00	150.00	175.00	225.00	275.00
*63	$5	Queen Victoria—Sailing Ship, payable at Montreal.	T. D. Harington	125.00	150.00	175.00	250.00	300.00
63a	$5	Same, but payable at Toronto	T. D. Harington	125.00	150.00	200.00	250.00	300.00
63b	$5	Same, but payable at Halifax	T. D. Harington	150.00	200.00	250.00	300.00	375.00

No.	Note	Portrait, Design, Etc.	Signatures	V.G.	Fine	V.F.	E.F.	Unc.
64	$10	Discovery of Land—Beaver, payable at Montreal....	T. D. Harington	175.00	225.00	275.00	325.00	400.00
64a	$10	Same, but payable at Toronto........	T. D. Harington	175.00	225.00	275.00	325.00	400.00
64b	$10	Same, but payable at Halifax........	T. D. Harington	200.00	275.00	325.00	400.00	500.00
65	$20	Beavers at work; Portraits at left and right......	T. D. Harington	300.00	375.00	425.00	500.00	600.00
66	$50	Allegorical Vignette, same as on $50. Dom. of Canada, payable at Toronto......	T. D. Harington	400.00	475.00	525.00	600.00	700.00
67	$100	Queen Victoria, payable at Montreal......	T. D. Harington	500.00	575.00	625.00	700.00	900.00
68	$500	Female seated beside Arms & Lion, payable Montreal.	T. D. Harington	750.00	900.00	1,000	1,200	1,500

NEWFOUNDLAND NOTES

For many years before its entry into Confederation in 1949, Newfoundland bore the proud title of "The Oldest Colony." It was discovered by John Cabot, who took formal possession of the island in the name of Henry VII, under whose letters patent the voyage had been undertaken, on June 24, 1497.

For many years, the colony was considered to consist of the Island of Newfoundland and a portion of the coast of Labrador which, although not actually delimited, was generally considered to comprise a narrow strip along the coast. In 1925, however, the matter was referred to the Privy Council, which decided in 1927 that the true boundary extended broadly to the height of land from which waters flowed towards the Atlantic. This decision enormously increased the area of the colony, although the newly acquired territory was largely barren, and most difficult of access. However, the recent development of the great Knob Lake iron ore deposits appears to presage a more important role for the area.

Newfoundland was the earliest Dominion to achieve self-government (1855). In 1934, however, the colony fell into serious financial difficulties, and temporarily surrendered its autonomy to the United Kingdom, which set up a commission to get the country back on its feet. This state of affairs continued until 1949, when the colony became Canada's tenth province, following a plebiscite.

70

78

NEWFOUNDLAND GOVERNMENT CASH NOTES

Denom.	1901	1902	1903	1904	1905	1906	1907	1908	1909	V.G.	Fine	V.F.	Unc.
40¢	69	*70	71	72	73	74	75	76	77	60.00	80.00	100.00	175.00
50¢	*78	79	80	81	82	83	84	85	86	50.00	70.00	90.00	150.00
80¢	87	*88	89	90	91	92	93	94	95	60.00	80.00	100.00	175.00
$1.	96	97	*98	99	100	101	102	103	104	100.00	125.00	150.00	200.00
$5.	105	106	107	108	109	110	111	*112	113	150.00	200.00	250.00	300.00

98

117

88

112

122

130

120

127

Denom.	1910-1911	1911-1912	1912-1913	1913-1914	V. G.	Fine	V. F.	E. F.	Unc.
25¢	114	115	116	*117	25.00	30.00	35.00	40.00	65.00
50¢	118	119	*120	121	28.00	33.00	40.00	50.00	75.00
$1.	*122	123	124	125	50.00	60.00	70.00	80.00	125.00
$2.	126	*127	128	129	75.00	95.00	125.00	150.00	200.00
$5.	*130	131	132	133	100.00	150.00	200.00	250.00	300.00
$1.	*134	Jan. 2, 1920 King George V			20.00	30.00	40.00	50.00	150.00
$2.	*135	Jan. 2, 1920			35.00	45.00	60.00	90.00	200.00

NEWFOUNDLAND NOTES

134   135

BANK OF CANADA NOTES

During January, 1950 the 10 Canadian chartered banks paid over to the Bank of Canada the balances outstanding in their note circulation accounts as at December 31, 1949, and henceforth the government-owned bank became liable for all notes of the chartered banks still in the hands of the public, amounting to $13,302,046.60.

That was the final step in the 15-year program under which the Bank of Canada assumed the entire issuing function of the country and wrote "finis" to an important, sometimes tempestuous, chapter of Canadian banking history.

136   137

BANK OF CANADA
FIRST ISSUE 1935

The 1935 issue consisted of separate English and French text notes which have the same signatures J. A. C. Osborne and G. F. Towers. All later issues are bilingual.

No.		English Text	V.G.	Fine	V.F.	E.F.	Unc.
*136	$1	King George V	3.50	5.00	6.00	7.00	11.00
*137	$2	Queen Mary	4.50	6.00	7.00	9.00	15.00

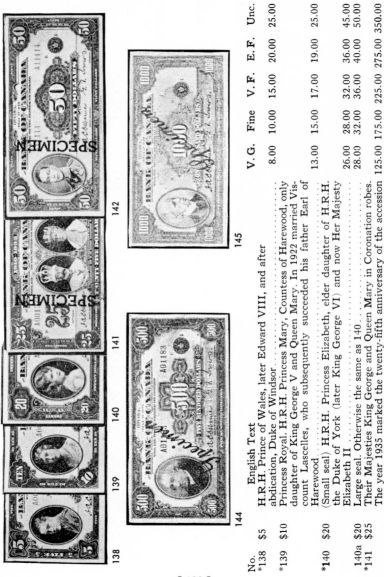

No.		English Text	V.G.	Fine	V.F.	E.F.	Unc.
*138	$5	H.R.H. Prince of Wales, later Edward VIII, and after abdication, Duke of Windsor	8.00	10.00	15.00	20.00	25.00
*139	$10	Princess Royal. H.R.H. Princess Mary, Countess of Harewood, only daughter of King George V and Queen Mary. In 1922 married Viscount Lascelles, who subsequently succeeded his father Earl of Harewood	13.00	15.00	17.00	19.00	25.00
*140	$20	(Small seal) H.R.H. Princess Elizabeth, elder daughter of H.R.H. the Duke of York (later King George VI) and now Her Majesty Elizabeth II	26.00	28.00	32.00	36.00	45.00
140a	$20	Large seal. Otherwise the same as 140	28.00	32.00	36.00	40.00	50.00
*141	$25	Their Majesties King George and Queen Mary in Coronation robes. The year 1935 marked the twenty-fifth anniversary of the accession	125.00	175.00	225.00	275.00	350.00

of King George V. The issue is sometimes referred to as the "Silver Jubilee" issue, but the presence of the portraits of Sir J. A. Macdonald and Sir W. Laurier on the two high values sufficiently indicates the inaccuracy of the appellation. The $25. note, however, (the only issue of this denomination) undoubtedly was intended as a commemoration of the event. The view of Windsor Castle on the reverse alludes to the fact that, during World War I, the name "Windsor" was officially adopted for the Royal House of Great Britain. There was a total issue of 140,000 of these notes with the serial letter "A."

BANK OF CANADA NOTES

ENGLISH TEXT

No.			V. G.	Fine	V. F.	E. F.	Unc.
*142	$50.	H.R.H. the Duke of York, second son of King George and Queen Mary. Ascended the throne as King George VI on the abdication of his brother, King Edward VIII in December, 1936	60.00	65.00	70.00	80.00	90.00
143	$100.	H.R.H. the Duke of Gloucester, third son of King George V and Queen Mary	115.00	120.00	125.00	130.00	140.00
*144	$500.	Sir John A. Macdonald, K.C.B. first Prime Minister of the Dominion of Canada in 1867, and holder of that office (except for 1873-78 term) until his death in 1891. He was the leader of the Conservative party	525.00	550.00	575.00	600.00	650.00
*145	$1000.	Sir Wilfred Laurier, P.C., G.C.M.G. was Prime Minister of the Dominion of Canada from 1896 to 1911. He was leader of the Liberal party for 31 years, and sat in the House of Commons for 45 years, following three years in the Quebec Legislative Assembly	1025.00	1050.00	1075.00	1100.00	1150.00

BANK OF CANADA NOTES

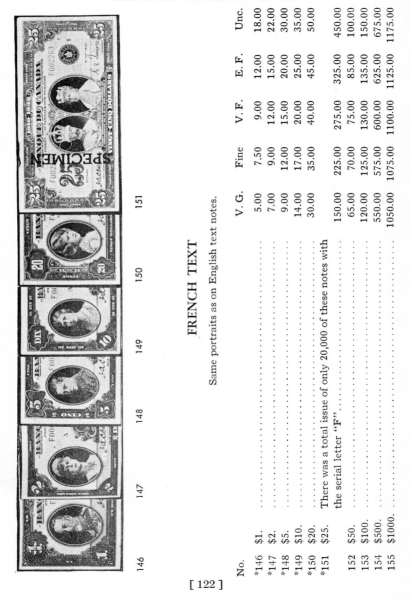

FRENCH TEXT

Same portraits as on English text notes.

No.		V. G.	Fine	V. F.	E. F.	Unc.
*146	$1.	5.00	7.50	9.00	12.00	18.00
*147	$2.	7.00	9.00	12.00	15.00	22.00
*148	$5.	9.00	12.00	15.00	20.00	30.00
*149	$10.	14.00	17.00	20.00	25.00	35.00
*150	$20.	30.00	35.00	40.00	45.00	50.00
*151	$25.	There was a total issue of only 20,000 of these notes with the serial letter "F".				
152	$50.	150.00	225.00	275.00	325.00	450.00
153	$100.	65.00	70.00	75.00	85.00	100.00
154	$500.	120.00	125.00	130.00	135.00	150.00
155	$1000.	550.00	575.00	600.00	625.00	675.00
		1050.00	1075.00	1100.00	1125.00	1175.00

146 147 148 149 150 151

BANK OF CANADA NOTES

BANK OF CANADA 1937 ISSUE — George VI

All notes except the $100 and $1000 denominations have a portrait of George VI. The $100 note has a portrait of Sir John A. Macdonald, and the $1000 denomination one of Sir Wilfred Laurier.

J. A. C. Osborne — G. F. Towers Signatures

		Fine	V. F.	E. F.	Unc.
156	$1.	5.00	7.50	10.00	15.00
157	$2.	7.00	8.50	10.00	15.00
158	$5.	10.00	13.00	18.00	25.00
159	$10.	15.00	17.00	20.00	25.00
160	$20.	25.00	27.00	30.00	35.00
161	$50.	60.00	65.00	70.00	80.00
162	$100.	125.00	135.00	150.00	175.00
163	$1000.	1050.00	1075.00	1100.00	1125.00

D. Gordon — G. F. Towers Signatures.

		Fine	V. F.	E. F.	Unc.
164	$1.	2.50	3.50	4.50	7.00
165	$2.	3.50	5.00	6.50	10.00
166	$5.	7.50	9.00	15.00	15.00
167	$10.	12.00	15.00	16.50	20.00
168	$20.	23.00	25.00	27.00	30.00
169	$50.	55.00	60.00	65.00	75.00
170	$100.	110.00	115.00	125.00	135.00
171	$1000.	1025.00	1050.00	1075.00	1100.00

J. E. Coyne — G. F. Towers Signatures.

		Fine	V. F.	E. F.	Unc.
*172	$1.	2.00	2.25	3.00	4.00
173	$2.	3.00	4.00	5.00	7.00
174	$5.	7.00	8.00	9.00	11.00
175	$10.	12.00	13.00	14.00	17.00
176	$20.	22.00	24.00	26.00	30.00
177	$50.	55.00	60.00	65.00	75.00
178	$100.	110.00	115.00	120.00	130.00
179	$1000.	1025.00	1035.00	1050.00	1075.00

172

180

BANK OF CANADA 1954 ISSUE — Queen Elizabeth II

J. E. Coyne — G. F. Towers Signatures (Devil's Face Variety)

Soon after the appearance of these notes, a resemblance to a devil's face was noticed in the Queen's hair behind the left ear. Owing to protests, revisions were made in the engraving to remove the objectionable feature from all denominations. However, the change did not take place until the Coyne-Towers issue was completed and the Beattie Coyne issue commenced.

		Fine	V.F.	E.F.	Unc.
*180	$1.	1.25	1.50	1.75	3.00
181	$2.	3.00	3.50	4.00	6.00
182	$5.	6.00	7.00	8.00	10.00
183	$10.	11.00	12.00	13.00	15.00

		Fine	V.F.	E.F.	Unc.
184	$20.	21.00	22.00	23.00	25.00
185	$50.	53.00	55.00	56.00	60.00
186	$100.	105.00	110.00	115.00	125.00
187	$1000.	1010.00	1015.00	1025.00	1050.00

J. R. Beattie — J. E. Coyne Signatures (Devil's Face Variety)

		Fine	V.F.	E.F.	Unc.
188	$1.	1.25	1.50	1.75	3.00
189	$2.	2.50	3.00	4.00	6.00
190	$5.	6.00	7.00	8.00	10.00
191	$10.	11.00	12.00	13.00	15.00

		Fine	V.F.	E.F.	Unc.
192	$20.	22.00	23.00	24.00	26.00
193	$50.	53.00	55.00	57.00	60.00
193	$100.	105.00	110.00	115.00	125.00
194	$1000.	1010.00	1015.00	1025.00	1050.00

J. R. Beattie — J. E. Coyne Signatures (Without Devil's Face)

195

		Fine	V. F.	E. F.	Unc.
*195	$1.	1.25	1.50	1.75	2.00
196	$2.	2.25	2.50	3.00	4.00
197	$5.	5.35	5.50	6.00	7.00
198	$10.	10.35	10.50	11.00	12.00
199	$20.	20.50	21.00	22.00	23.00
200	$50.	51.00	52.00	53.00	55.00
201	$100.	103.00	105.00	110.00	115.00
202	$1000.	1015.00	1020.00	1025.00	1035.00

J. R. Beattie — L. Rasminsky Signatures

203	$1.
204	$2.
205	$5.
206	$10.
207	$20.
208	$50.
209	$100.
210	$1000.

At the time of going to press the $1, $2, $5, $10 and $20 denominations have been released for circulation. Other denominations will follow as required.

Asterisk Notes.

An asterisk preceding the serial number indicates that the notes are replacements for defective ones removed and destroyed in the printing process. Usual premium on the 1954 issue ranges from $1 for V. G. to $2 to $5 for Unc.

These notes are very scarce and are seldom found in circulation. They exist for all signature and vignette varieties.

INDEX

COIN FOLDERS

A Convenient Method
for Housing Your Collection

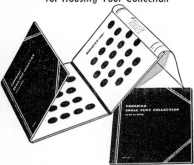

Made in two tones of blue . . . printed in black and silver, giving a brilliant "Jewel Case" effect to your coin collection.
Made by WHITMAN   Size Folded 5¾" x 7½"

COMPLETE LIST OF STYLES
UNITED STATES
Large Cent — 1793 to 1825
Large Cent — 1826 to 1857
Indian-Eagle Cents — 1856 to 1909
Lincoln Head Cent — 1909 to 1940
Lincoln Head Cent — Starting 1941
Lincoln Memorial Cent — Starting 1959
Cents — Plain, no printing

Half Dime — 1794 to 1873
Shield Type Nickel — 1866 to 1883
Liberty Head Nickel — 1883 to 1913
Buffalo Nickel — 1913 to 1938
Jefferson Nickel — 1938 to 1961
Jefferson Nickel — Starting 1962
Nickels — Plain, no printing

Bust Type Dime — 1796 to 1837
Liberty Seated Dime — 1837 to 1862
Liberty Seated Dime — 1863 to 1891
Barber Dime — 1892 to 1916
Mercury Head Dime — 1916 to 1945
Roosevelt Dime — Starting 1946
Dimes — Plain, no printing

Liberty Seated Quarter — 1838 to 1865
Liberty Seated Quarter — 1866 to 1891
Barber Quarter — 1892 to 1905
Barber Quarter — 1906 to 1916
Lib. Standing Quarter — 1916 to 1930
Wash. Head Quarter — 1932 to 1945
Wash. Head Quarter — 1946 to 1959
Wash. Head Quarter — Starting 1960
Quarters — Plain, no printing

Lib. Seated Half Dollar — 1839 to 1850
Lib. Seated Half Dollar — 1851 to 1862
Lib. Seated Half Dollar — 1863 to 1873
Lib. Seated Half Dollar — 1873 to 1891
Barber Half Dollar — 1892 to 1903
Barber Half Dollar — 1904 to 1915
Lib. Standing Half Dollar — 1916 to 1936
Lib. Standing Half Dollar — 1937 to 1947
Ben. Franklin Half Dollar — 1948-1963
Kennedy Half Dollar — Starting 1964
Halves — Plain, no printing

Morgan Dollar — 1878 to 1883
Morgan Dollar — 1884 to 1890

Morgan Dollar — 1891 to 1897
Morgan Dollar — 1898 to 1921
Peace Dollar — 1921 to 1935
Dollars — Plain, no printing

MISCELLANEOUS
Half Cent — 1793 to 1857
Silver Three Cent — 1851 to 1873
Two Cent — Nickel Three Cent — 1864 to 1889
Type Coins, Small Denominations
Type Coins, Large Denominations
20th Century Type Coins

ONE-A-YEAR
Cents, 1909 to Date
Nickels, 1913 to Date
Dimes, 1916 to Date
Quarters, 1916 to Date

CANADA
Large Cents — 1858 to 1920
Small Cents — Starting 1920
Silver Five Cents — 1858 to 1921
Nickels — 1922-1960
Nickels — Starting 1961
Dimes — 1858 to 1936
Dimes — Starting 1937
Quarters — 1858 to 1910
Quarters — 1911 to 1952
Quarters — Starting 1953
Halves — 1870 to 1910
Halves — 1911 to 1936
Halves — 1937-1960
Halves — Starting 1961
Silver Dollars — 1935 to 1957
Silver Dollars — Starting 1958
Quarters — Plain, no printing
Halves — Plain, no printing
Canada Coin Type Collection
Dollars — Plain, no printing

NEWFOUNDLAND
Cents & Half Cents — Newfoundland, New Brunswick, Nova Scotia and Prince Edward Island
Newfoundland 5¢ — 1865 to 1947
N. Brunswick 5-10-20¢ — 1862 to 1864
Newfoundland 10¢ — 1865 to 1947
Newfoundland 20-25¢ — 1865 to 1919
Newfoundland 50¢ — 1870 to 1919
Newfoundland Coin Type Collection

GREAT BRITAIN
Farthings — 1860 to 1901
Farthings — 1902 to 1936
Farthings — 1937 to 1956
Halfpennies — 1860 to 1901
Halfpennies — 1902 to 1936
Halfpennies — Starting 1937
Pennies — 1860 to 1880
Pennies — 1881 to 1901
Pennies — 1902 to 1929
Pennies — Starting 1930
Threepence Silver — 1838 to 1901
Threepence Silver — 1902 to 1945
Threepence Brass — Starting 1937
Sixpence — 1902 to 1936
Sixpence — Starting 1937
Shillings — 1902 to 1936
Shillings — 1937 to 1951
Shillings — Starting 1953

MEXICO
One Centavo — Starting 1905
Five Centavos — 1905 to 1955
Five Centavos — Starting 1954